# Introduction to Modern

# Elementary Mathematics

## the author...

Ladis D. Kovach is Professor of Mathematics and Chairman of the Department of Mathematics and Physics at Pepperdine College. He received the B.S. in physics and the M.S. in mathematics from Case Institute of Technology, the M.A. in education from Western Reserve University, and the Ph.D. in mathematics from Purdue University. His areas of specialization consist of computers, analog simulation, applied mathematics, and teacher education, in which he is well qualified with considerable background as a teacher and as a professional electrical engineer.

Dr. Kovach is a member of numerous professional societies, including the Mathematical Association of America, theAmerican Physical Society, and L'Association Internationale pour le Calcul Analogique. He has published more than twenty papers on mathematics education and on the analog computer, and is the author of Holden-Day's *Computer-Oriented Mathematics*. Since 1960 he has lectured extensively to parents, teachers, and students on the subject of Modern Elementary Mathematics.

# Introduction to Modern

# Elementary Mathematics

by *LADIS D. KOVACH*, Pepperdine College

HOLDEN-DAY, INC., 1966

*San Francisco · London · Amsterdam*

*To Narda and the boys—*
*Paul, Andrew, and Matthew*

# Preface

Professor George Polya of Stanford University once said that he heard teachers complain about certain mathematics education courses they took as being "thin soup without any meat." He also heard complaints about certain mathematics courses as being "steak which is too tough to chew." The plight of the elementary teacher is summed up here — he[1] has had a choice between these two extremes in mathematics.

This book will provide a happy medium between these two extremes— a "stew," if you like. We will develop those topics in mathematics which are likely to be new to the elementary teacher, but we will do it in a *spiral fashion*. This means that the reader's first contact with a new topic will be somewhat perfunctory. In other words, he will be introduced to the basic idea and become familiar with the vocabulary to a certain extent.

The next time he meets this same topic, he will be asked not only to review what has gone before, but to carry the idea forward and look at it in a more sophisticated fashion. By repeating this procedure two or three times we hope to bring even the student with the weakest background in mathematics up to a fairly high level. We hope that he will be able to understand, appreciate, and teach these basic topics to his students.

Accordingly the book has been arranged in a novel fashion. For example, we find chapters 1, 5, and 9 all entitled, "Sets." Each one contains a discussion of the subject *up to a certain point*. In fact, the book could very well have been entitled, "The *ABC*'s of Modern

---

[1] Contrary to past custom, we prefer to use the generic term "he" for the elementary teacher. We hope that this will not prove offensive to the many wonderful women teachers.

Mathematics." This implies — quite correctly — that the reader who has mastered the A, B, and C chapters on geometry (to name one) still has 23 letters to go in that subject.

On the other hand, a parent or administrator may be content to study only the "A" chapters. Some readers may be grateful that they can find a book on "modern" (or "contemporary" — an equally proper and far more durable term) mathematics which *doesn't* present them with more than they really want to know about the subject.

The A, B, and C chapters have been taught to classes of both pre-service and in-service teachers, supervisors, administrators, parents, and children. Each set of four chapters comprised a one semester-hour course. With the addition of the introduction and chapters 13, 14 and 15 the book is suitable for a three or four semester-hour course for students of widely varying backgrounds in mathematics. If necessary, the "A" chapters can be used with teachers of grades K to 3 who may then study the "B" chapters on their own in order to gain some depth in the topics.

Much of the material in this book was first taught during the summer of 1961. Since then courses have been scheduled on Saturday mornings during the academic year as well as during the summers. Many of the students were understandably timid about mathematics and especially about "the new math." Some of them had weak backgrounds in traditional mathematics while others had been exposed to courses where rigor was the order of the day. We decided to prepare a set of notes that would convey the spirit of modern mathematics teaching without attempting to convert the students to mathematics majors or assuming that the conversion had already taken place.

Our experience with the notes from which this book was written was most gratifying. We found that our students were highly motivated, interested in the material, and anxious to present it to their students. We sincerely hope that you, too, have these qualities.

Special thanks are due Mr. Fred Locarnini and Mrs. Nellie Orphanidis for their help in the preparation of the manuscript. Honorable mention must also be given to the helpful, cooperative staff of the publisher.

*Ladis D. Kovach*

# Table of Contents

# Introduction

## 1. Why *new* mathematics?

You've heard the expression, "Times aren't like they used to be." Perhaps you've even said this yourself and if someone were to ask you to be more specific, you might say, "Well, for one thing, newspapers aren't like they used to be—they're making the print much smaller nowadays"; or, "They're making belts and collars a lot tighter than they used to"; or, perhaps, "Staircases are steeper than they used to be"; or, "The distance to the corner bus stop is farther than it used to be."

And now to these troubles is added another one. They're not making arithmetic the way they used to. Parents are finding that they can no longer help their children with their arithmetic homework. It seems that the reason for this is *the new mathematics*. For some reason— known only to mathematicians?—the whole business of arithmetic has been turned topsy-turvy. The system that has been adequate for hundreds of years is no longer adequate. Pupils must learn new concepts, new words, new methods. And, of course, before the pupils can learn these things the teacher must learn them also. It is no wonder that one over-worked, frustrated teacher said recently, "It's bad enough to be living in an age of anxiety and devastating uncertainty— and now this new math on top of everything!"

It does seem so entirely unnecessary, doesn't it? But we are going to try to give you some idea of *why* the new mathematics came into being and what it's all about.

In the past—meaning when *we* were in elementary school—the emphasis was on speed and accuracy in manipulating numbers. We learned certain methods and became quite proficient in arithmetic skills. We also learned certain rules which we followed blindly. Some of you may remember one or two of those rules. For example, "Invert the divisor and multiply," or "to change a decimal to a percent move the decimal point two places to the right." We followed these rules blindly and whatever the teacher said was *the law*. It never occurred to any of us to question *why* a certain method produced the correct answer. The teacher said to do it a certain way and that was good enough for us. And, strangely enough, most of us managed to get good grades in arithmetic. In other words, we learned our arithmetic skills quite well.

The next step was to go from arithmetic to algebra. Now many of us found to our sorrow that our skill in manipulating *numbers* did not help much in algebra. Here we had to manipulate *letters* and *equations*. This was much more difficult; we had to learn more rules and these rules became more mysterious and more confusing. For example, "a minus times a minus is a plus," or "change the sign of the subtrahend and add," or "transpose the unknown to the left side of the equation and the numbers to the right side." The fact that we didn't understand most of these rules didn't really matter. We learned them and we learned how to manipulate letters and equations. That is, *some* of us did. Others fell by the wayside and decided that mathematics was not for them—they were not cut out for it. This feeling was quite general among girls who very often justified their failure by saying that no one in their family was any good in algebra and they weren't about to be the exception.

The hardy ones who survived their first encounter with high school algebra went on to geometry. We found in geometry that our skill in manipulating numbers and our knowledge that "two minuses make a plus" did not seem to help us very much here. Geometry turned out to be an entirely different sort of business, consisting of strange things like theorems, axioms, propositions, and corollaries. Many students never did learn the difference between these. Those of us who were ambitious amd worked hard learned the theorems and memorized the proofs. We could say, for example, that the reason two angles were equal was because of "proposition 14, page 74." Or we wrote as the reason for some statement, "by Corollary 5." Again the mortality rate was quite high and a large percentage of those who survived algebra succumbed to geometry. In fact, the only ones left at the end of 10th grade geometry were a few individuals who were pointed toward college to become mathematics majors or scientists.

It is hardly worth considering these "last of the Mohicans," but we will continue. After geometry came more algebra and then more geometry but there's no use talking any more about these. Let's go on to trigonometry. In this subject we studied triangles and the relationships between the angles and the sides of these triangles. We found again, unfortunately, that neither our skill in manipulating numbers, nor our skill in "transposing," nor our ability to recite theorems did us much good in trigonometry. We had to start from scratch and work very hard in order to pass this course. A few more students fell by the wayside, but not too many, because most of them got lost in mathematics back at the previous two levels.

Those of us who survived high school mathematics and went on to college came face to face with calculus. What happened here is now ancient history. It's a repetition of the same things that we encountered before. Again we lost a large number of students. Some of these decided to go to a technical institute and learn a trade, while others changed their majors.

You can see what kind of a mathematical structure we have built here. It is certainly not a stable one. There is danger at any instant that the whole thing will topple and come crashing to the ground. It is to prevent this toppling, to build a more *stable* structure, that we are changing our methods of teaching mathematics. We are trying to change our method of teaching mathematics so that the broadest part of mathematics education is at the base, so that we can have something to build upon. This broadest part, of course, comes during the elementary school period.

Usually about this time someone will ask the question, "Most pupils do *not* become mathematics majors, so why get all excited about building a good foundation in mathematics?" The main reasons are that the growth of science and technology in recent years has made it necessary for the intelligent citizen to know more about these subjects. Since science is based on mathematics, and can hardly be understood without a knowledge of mathematics, an understanding of mathematics is essential to everyone. Another factor is the widespread use today of electronic computers. A large percentage of our population is either directly connected with computers or has someone in its immediate circle of family or friends who is. Some of these people may be using computers for business applications, some for scientific applications, some may be maintaining or servicing computers, and some may be writing programs for computers. In other words, we have an entirely new industry today and since so many people are involved in this, it becomes necessary for *everyone* to know something about it in order to talk intelligently.

The availability of the electronic computer has made mathematics more useful to people who before had no need for it. Today we find that social scientists, doctors of medicine, biologists, economists, businessmen, and even home economists and physical educators are using the computer to solve specialized problems in their fields. Of course, this requires that they have a greater knowledge of mathematics than was necessary in former years.

The rapid growth of science and technology in recent years has been due, in part, to advances in mathematics and the utilization of the electronic computer. In order to design complex systems[1] it is mandatory that a mathematical model be built first and the various characteristics of the system be analyzed on a computer. It is also essential that the mathematical model be as true to life as possible and this is most difficult to achieve. The many different and unpredictable things that can affect the operation of a system require that the most sophisticated mathematics be used in the analysis.

Then, too, there have been some new types of mathematics that have been developed. *Linear programming*, that is, the branch of mathematics concerned with solving simultaneously a system of inequalities, is useful in a variety of situations. Its application ranges from a determination of the most efficient supply system for the armed forces of a nation to the determination of the types and amounts of food needed by a hospital to provide the necessary nutrients most economically. *Graph theory*, a branch of combinatorial topology, has developed recently and is useful in analyzing complex electrical circuits. Thus, today more mathematics is required for careers in science and

---

[1] By a "system" is meant the totality of equipment and knowledge needed to accomplish a certain task, such as, making a landing on the moon, making observations from a satellite, or installing an automatic traffic control system.

engineering *and* also in many other fields. Today a higher percentage of our pupils will need to study more advanced mathematics. If they do not get a solid foundation in the elementary school, they may be handicapped later.

To summarize, mathematics was formerly taught in a way that tended to emphasize *skills* and to ignore real *understanding*. Knowledge gained in this way was almost impossible to extend. Yet, better training in mathematics is necessary in both technical and nontechnical fields today. Moreover, the intelligent citizen must have a better understanding of science and technology since rapid developments in these areas are affecting him personally as well as influencing national policies.

## 2. History of some modern programs

There is some danger in the use of the word "modern" in connection with mathematics programs. It implies that we are in some sort of experimental phase. Actually, the "experimenting" was done in approximately the decade between 1950 and 1960. During this time new methods and new materials were tried out in experimental classrooms all over the United States. Many teachers spent extra hours on Saturdays, after school, early in the morning to become familiar with new concepts so that they could teach them to their classes. On the basis of these experiments, carried out by hundreds of teachers in thousands of classes, new elementary mathematics textbooks were written. These books are available today and are being enthusiastically adopted all over the country. In fact, the decade from 1960 to 1970 might be called the *implementation* decade in contrast to the previous *experimental* decade.

In this section we will describe some of the more famous of the modern programs. We believe that in this way we can convey to you some of the spirit of modern mathematics. We call your attention, however, to an important point. While on the surface it may *seem* that the various programs differ considerably in their approach and treatment, we will show in the next section that there are points of similarity which are quite important. With this in mind, you may discover these similarities yourself as you read.

# School Mathematics Study Group (SMSG)

Although not a pioneering group, the SMSG is perhaps the best known because it has had more members, more experimental classes, and has produced more publications than any other group. SMSG has probably inspired the writing of more textbooks than any other organization.

A brief history of SMSG can, perhaps, best be given by quoting from a government publication.[2]

---

Consideration of the mathematics programs at the elementary school level by the School Mathematics Study Group began with a conference on elementary school mathematics called in 1959 by Professor E. G. Begle, director of the project. In attendance were university professors of mathematics, high school and elementary school teachers, supervisors and education specialists with specific interest in mathematics, psychologists, and representatives from scientific and governmental organizations having an interest in mathematics. From this conference came the recommendation that a critical study of elementary school mathematics curriculum be undertaken. Among the aspects of the total elementary mathematics program suggested for study were: (1) the grade placement of topics; (2) development of concepts and mathematical principles; (3) the possible introduction of new topics particularly from geometry; (4) topics for able learners; (5) training for teachers; (6) the relation of elementary school mathematics to future study of the subject; (7) methods and materials for effective classroom instruction; and (8) the application of findings on concept-formation from psychology and child development to the learning of mathematics.

In March of 1960, a detailed outline of a suggested program for grades 4, 5, and 6 was developed. For 8 weeks during the summer of 1960 a writing team composed of classroom teachers or supervisors, mathematicians, and mathematics educators worked together to prepare materials. At this time units comprising a complete course for grade 4 and sample units for grades 5 and 6 with accompanying teachers' manuals were prepared. The format of the units is the "write-in" text workbook type with explanation and instruction; space is allowed for

---

[2] "Elementary School Mathematics: New Directions" by Edwina Deans, U. S. Department of Health, Education, and Welfare; U. S. Government Printing Office, 1963, no. OE-29042.

pupil answers, for completion of exercises, or for carrying out activities. In this tentative form tryouts were held in 27 experimental centers over the country involving around 12 000 students and 150 fourth-grade, 110 fifth-grade, and 110 sixth-grade teachers. Each center was associated with a college or university which provided consultant service for the participating teachers. Regular meetings were held to build the mathematics background for units to be presented and to evaluate those which had been taught. In evaluating each unit teachers were requested to give reactions to the appropriateness of sequence and grade level of each unit, the difficulty of the material from the standpoint of concept development and reading and the amount of time devoted to teaching the unit, the use of supplementary materials or additional practice exercises, and the effectiveness of the teacher's commentary. On the basis of the experiences of the participating teachers and their evaluations, the units were revised and completed during the summer of 1961 and tried out again during 1961–1962.

According to the committee, the proposed SMSG curriculum is not radically different from the regular present-day program in its organization. The present program is viewed as being based on social applications while the goal of the proposed changes of the SMSG is to provide a curriculum based on mathematics. There are some new topics and new approaches to old ideas. The SMSG committee believes that a healthy fusion of the old and the new will lead students to a better understanding of the basic concepts and structure of mathematics and will provide a firmer foundation for understanding and use of mathematics. The committee hopes that the materials they have prepared will serve as models and as a source of suggestions for textbook authors and as aids in preservice and inservice teacher education programs.

Another point of view held by the committee is that skill in computation and insight go hand in hand in mathematics, both being essential to proficiency. Emphasis is placed on precision of language of mathematics and on knowledge of and appreciation for a mathematical system which expands gradually to make more and more mathematical solutions possible.

In an effort which is national in scope, the School Mathematics Study Group has research and development in the teaching of school mathematics as its primary purpose. It expects to continue to develop courses, teaching materials, and teaching methods; to promote inservice education; and to carry out long-term evaluations of its mathematics programs.

# Greater Cleveland Mathematics Program (GCMP)

In the same year that SMSG got started (1959) another group in Cleveland, Ohio was formed. Their purposes and the manner in which they have set about to implement them are given in the following paragraphs[3]:

The Educational Research Council of Greater Cleveland, the parent organization of the Greater Cleveland Mathematics Program, is an independent, nonprofit organization which serves 25 school districts and 2 private schools in the greater Cleveland area. A major purpose of the Council is to develop the best possible curriculums, kindergarten through grade 12, and implement them immediately in the classrooms of the Council Schools.

In March 1959 the advisory committee, consisting of the superintendents of schools from the participating school districts, requested that the Council make a concerted effort to improve the mathematics curriculum. As a result, the Greater Cleveland Mathematics Program was initiated.

The purpose of the project is to develop a new elementary and secondary curriculum that can be presented to all children in a logical and systematic way so that they will completely understand the basic mathematical concepts before they are taught the computational schemes or algorisms.[4]

To accomplish its purpose effectively, the project makes extensive use of the discovery approach to learning. The project presents problem situations to students as if they had not been explored already by the great minds of the past and present. These situations are presented in such a manner that discovery has a good chance of taking place spontaneously; then students are led to the established symbolism. The logical structure of mathematics stimulates the imagination of children and leads them to appreciate mathematics as a dynamic and meaningful study by letting them experience the thrill of discovering or recreating some mathematics for themselves.

Personnel involved in the development and field testing of the materials include mathematicians, mathematics educators, consultants in mathematics, classroom teachers, elementary mathematics supervisors, and administrators.

During the first year of the project, teachers in the program were

[3] Op. cit.
[4] Also spelled "algorithms."

given foundation courses in mathematics by the project staff and received some materials to enrich their regular classroom program. The second year, teachers used the pupils' exercise sheet and teachers' guides which were prepared by writing teams of teachers and project staff members. These materials were revised during the spring and summer of the second and third years using feedback from approximately four hundred teachers per grade level.

A local television station has been used as a means of providing teacher training on mathematical content, teaching procedure, and the proper use of materials. Field assistants from the project are assigned to grade levels K to 3 and 4 to 6 to assist the teachers in the classrooms through classroom demonstrations, inservice meetings, and individual or grade-level conferences.

Enrichment topics at the fifth- and sixth-grade level extend the work on topics such as the following: products and factors; prime and composite numbers; geometry; sequences and series; simple informal proofs; and sentences, open sentences, and conditional statements.

## University of Illinois Arithmetic Project

The history and aims of this project differ substantially from the two previous programs described. This project is actually an outgrowth of the University of Illinois Committee on School Mathematics (UICSM) which was formed in 1951 because the university's School of Engineering was dissatisfied with the mathematics preparation of its entering students. The Arithmetic Project was a later outgrowth of the high-school project. Its aims and philosophy are contained in the following paragraphs [5]:

David A. Page, director of the University of Illinois Arithmetic Project, and his staff have attempted to devise materials to help children view work in mathematics as a fascinating adventure. By exposure to interesting and different ways of approaching familiar tasks, children are encouraged to make their own mathematics discoveries, to develop mathematical insight, and to acquire an intuitive understanding of many mathematics ideas which have usually been initiated much later in the child's school life. No claim is made that the methods employed are entirely new. Rather an effort is made to give all children the

[5] Op. cit.

opportunity to profit from the methods which some children and teachers have been using successfully all along.

In addition to working for better ways of presenting standard topics and attempting to adapt advanced topics for earlier use, the project team is inventing and developing new topics expressly for use in the early grades.

Although the materials prepared by the project are not recommended as a complete course of study, some topics are considered as a sequence for elementary classroom work and become the means whereby mathematical meanings for the processes of addition, subtraction, multiplication, and division with whole numbers and fractions are developed and practiced. They also serve as the vehicle through which algebraic and geometric ideas and other topics usually considered outside the province of elementary mathematics are introduced. Topics recommended for use as the need arises allow children to pursue mathematics beyond the usual limits of the elementary school. Project materials are prepared with two major purposes in mind: (1) to assist the teacher in learning mathematics and in acquiring the background of understanding necessary for successful teaching, and (2) to develop types of exercises and activities in mathematics which appear appropriate for elementary children as a result of experimentation in the classroom. Professor Page urges teachers who wish to learn more mathematics to work all of the exercises recommended for children as they examine and study the material. The main ideas are largely embedded in the exercises and often a sequence of exercises provides a hint at an important idea. He proposes that the teachers learn mathematics just as children do—by wrestling with it. The exercises will in turn help teachers to present a variety of basic mathematical ideas to their students. No grade level is specified, for the exercises have been taught successfully in project classes to children of different abilities and grade levels from first grade on when suitable adaptations were made for pace of instruction and difficulty of material. Work with experimental classes leads Professor Page to believe that considerably higher proficiency in computation can be obtained while at the same time a great deal of new, genuine mathematical content can be introduced. Exercises are therefore designed with a dual purpose: (1) to furnish much drill and practice on topics previously taught, and (2) to present new mathematical learning.

On the controversial question of terminology, the project team takes the position that ideas are more important than words and that an overemphasis on exact vocabulary may even interfere with concept development. For this reason a mixture of adult and classroom language is used to talk about the ideas to students. Few technical terms are used because the project teachers find that few are needed.

The project team has tried to develop activities which stimulate curiosity, exploration, experimentation, and discovery. Children are encouraged to estimate or approximate answers and to correct poor guesses. They are challenged to solve problems in different ways, to appreciate the many ways of arriving at an answer, to explain how they reason about a solution, and to respect the method requiring a high level of thought and reasoning. The material is characterized by less emphasis on computation and more on thinking and oral work. It is recognized that children learn best when they really want to find an answer and when the answer matters.

## Other Projects

Brief mention might also be made of the *Madison Project* which was begun in Madison Junior High School in Syracuse, New York, under the guidance of Professor Robert B. Davis of Syracuse University. In general, groups of children who start working with project materials are followed throughout the remainder of their school program. For this reason the project's work has expanded to include grades 2 through 9. Madison Project maintains the original center at Syracuse University where the project was initiated. More recently a second center has been developed at Webster College, Missouri. A significant feature of the Webster College participation is their undergraduate teacher education program designed to prepare teachers in the use of Madison Project materials.

The three major purposes of the program are: (1) to promote greater interest in mathematics; (2) to stimulate children to think more creatively about mathematics; and (3) to provide a sounder background for future mathematics.

The *Stanford Project* actually contains two separate ideas, one dealing with sets and numbers, and the other with geometry—both beginning at the early primary level. Professor Patrick Suppes of Stanford University, author of "Sets and Numbers," Books 1 through 6, for the elementary[6] grades, believes that all mathematics can be developed

[6] P. Suppes, *Sets and Numbers*, L. W. Singer, Syracuse, New York.

from notions of sets and operations on sets. His books are of the workbook type and require the selection of the appropriate set or the insertion of an answer to complete a mathematical sentence.

The results of experimental work begun in 1959–1960 indicated that the children had very little difficulty with either the notation or the vocabulary. During the 1960–1961 school year the material was used successfully in 25 first-grade classes representing a wide range of ability.

Professor Suppes and his colleague, Professor Newton S. Hawley, began the geometry project in the spring of 1958 when they taught geometry in a first-grade classroom 20 minutes per day for a period of two months. The high level of comprehension and achievement of the class encouraged the two to extend the project and write text materials.

### 3. Characteristics of modern mathematics teaching

If we examine the various texts that have been produced recently by different study groups, we notice a number of striking similarities. There are many characteristics that they have in common—although with varying degrees of emphasis. We define "modern mathematics teaching" as that which has these common characteristics. They are enumerated and discussed in the following paragraphs.

a. *Understanding* rather than *memorization* is emphasized. Many things that are memorized are soon forgotten if not used constantly. Rote learning without understanding is not the goal of mathematics education. There are a number of ways to deepen understanding in mathematics and some of them will be mentioned later in this outline.

b. *Language* and *vocabulary* are given much more care and emphasis. Terms such as "take away," "borrow," and "goes into" have been replaced with mathematical terms. It is not felt that the correct term must wait to be introduced until the pupil has matured, and that meanwhile a simple term must be used. Words like "rectangle," "square," "commutative" are easily understood by young children. After all, we don't describe an animal to a child in kindergarten by saying, "a big thing with a long nose," simply because this phrase contains only words of one syllable. No, we say "an elephant," and the children learn the word. *Commutative* is no stranger than *rhinoceros!*

Today's mathematics texts are to be *read*—they contain explanatory material and not just pictures and rules in bold-face type surrounded by a colored fence.

c. Mathematics can be more easily learned (and taught) if it is *unified*. Today we find arithmetic, algebra and geometry at all levels. We note that a book that used to be called, "Sixth Grade Arithmetic" is now probably, "Mathematics for Grade Six." This change is a result of the awareness that arithmetic is only one small part of the discipline known as "mathematics." Algebra and geometry are more readily accepted by young children because they approach new ideas with an open mind. They are not influenced by stories they've heard about how "hard" these subjects are.

d. Today's pupils are encouraged to *generalize*, to *experiment*, and to *discover*. It is no longer considered a mistake if a pupil solves a problem by a different method than the teacher. The teacher asks questions that will help a child bridge the gap between the particular and the general. He resists the temptation to "tell" the student, but rather lets him discover things for himself. This may seem like a slow, inefficient method of teaching but the fact remains that a person has an excellent chance of *rediscovering* something that he has forgotten, if he *discovered* it for himself in the first place.

e. Every computing scheme—or algorithm, as it is called—is presented with a *logical explanation* of why it works. The use of methods which cannot be justified logically is discouraged. In this connection, we encourage pupils to ask, "Why?" It is not felt that the teacher's authority should be sufficient reason for following a certain procedure in mathematics blindly.

f. One aspect of the modern method of teaching mathematics is to allow the pupils more freedom and thus to cater to *individual differences*. Modern mathematics is taught in such a way that pupils of varying abilities can proceed at their own rate. Allowing pupils to discover facts for themselves is an excellent way to accomplish this. A number of examples will be given in later chapters.

g. There is more attention given to the *history of mathematics* than in the past. Aside from the fact that the origins of mathematical symbols and methods is interesting in itself, this presents an opportunity to talk about mathematicians also. In this way the teacher can convey the valuable concept that mathematics was (and is being) developed by *people;* that it didn't spring up full-formed in some mysterious fashion.

h. Finally, and by no means least, *drill* is still emphasized in mathematics. The attitude towards drill, however, has changed. The belief is that a whole page of identical (except for different numbers) problems is not particularly inspiring to a child. One hundred addition problems might provide a challenge to the slow student but it will surely bore the average and bright student. A part of the new mathematics teaching is concerned with disguising drill as much as possible and keeping it interesting. This, too, will be illustrated in later chapters.

Of course, not all texts will emphasize the above eight characteristics to the same extent. Any text, however, which fails to consider more than one or two of the above traits is not in keeping with the modern point of view. We recommend the above list as criteria for choosing a modern text rather than simply looking in the Table of Contents to see whether the words "commutative" and "distributive" are mentioned.

# 1/Sets (A)

## 1. Element of a set

It has been a triumph of twentieth-century mathematicians to show that much if not all of mathematics can be developed from the basic ideas of sets. Thus it is no wonder that in modern mathematics teaching we talk about sets in kindergarten and in each succeeding grade right up through graduate school.

The meaning of a set in mathematics is similar to classification systems which are in use. For example, consider the following words:

| | |
|---|---|
| assembly | collection |
| squad | class |
| crowd | domain |
| horde | family |
| swarm | gang |
| school | group |
| covey | bundle |
| flock | mob |
| herd | ring |
| bunch | cluster |
| drove | set |
| . | . |
| . | . |
| . | . |

The three dots mean "and so on, in like fashion."

You may well wonder why the words in the above list were put in two columns (aside from saving space) and if there is any reason for putting a word in one column rather than in the other. Actually all of the words have to do with classifying various objects. The word "covey" brings to mind quail or partridge or birds, in general. The word "school," on the other hand, has to do with whales or porpoises or fish, in general.[1]

You will notice that every one of the words has to do with a grouping or classification of objects. In other words, each of the terms is a collective noun. The reason for the two columns is simply that the right-hand column contains words which are used in mathematics. One of these is the word **set.** A set is a collection or aggregate (to use still another term) of things or objects. The individual members of a set are called **elements.**

In mathematics we speak of a *set of numbers*. The elements of such a set are numbers. We can also speak of a set of lines in which case the elements are lines. A bunch of daisies can be thought of as a set of daisies, and here the elements are daisies. In other words, the concept of set is not restricted to mathematics.

We can speak of the set of boys in the class who are right-handed. The elements of such a set are the right-handed boys in that particular class. If the elements are to be those girls in the class who have brown hair, we can speak of the set of brown-haired girls in the class.

It is important to point out that the elements of a set need not be individuals, but may themselves be sets. For example, when we speak of the Los Angeles Dodgers,[2] we actually mean a set of professional baseball players. The elements in this set are the individual players. When we speak of the National League, however, we are referring to a set of ten *teams*. Here, each team is an *element* of the set. In other words, an element of a set may be a set itself. We will see later that this is the sort of situation that exists when we speak of a *set of lines* since each line is itself a set (of points).

## 2. Belonging or not belonging

It is often an important question whether a person belongs to the set

[1] We would not blame a teacher for objecting to our referring to a *school* as a collection of *fish*, but the usual definition in this case would spoil our example.

[2] Please feel free to replace this with your favorite team.

of people invited to a party or to the set of people who like the latest type of singing. In a given situation there are those who belong and those who do not. One cannot simultaneously be an element of a set and also not an element. In fact, it is essential to distinguish the elements of a set from the "non-elements."

We use the symbol $\in$ to mean "is an element of." We also use braces $\{\ \}$ to denote sets. Thus

$$\text{Mary} \in \{\text{brown-haired girls in the class}\},$$

would be read, "Mary is an element of the set of brown-haired girls in the class." Also,

$$\text{Frank} \notin \{\text{right-handed boys in the class}\},$$

would be read, "Frank is *not* an element of the set of right-handed boys in the class."

After writing out a number of such statements one begins to appreciate the use of symbols as a short-cut. It would be much more convenient, for example, to shorten the first statement to

$$m \in B$$

by letting $m$ represent Mary and $B$ represent the brown-haired girls in the class. The second statement might be shortened to

$$f \notin R$$

in a similar fashion.

Notice that the symbolic statements are almost meaningless by themselves. If you were to show these symbolic statements to the uninitiated (defined as one who has not read the previous pages) he would likely throw up his hands in despair. Much worse, he might spread the word that mathematics was "all Greek" to him. This is one way that rumors about the difficulty of mathematics get started.

Once you have the Rosetta stone in your possession, however, you no longer flinch when you see

$$j \notin R.$$

You know immediately that this is a statement referring to a *left-handed boy* in the class. The letter $j$ identifies him as John. If there are two left-handed boys in the class with the same initial, say John and

James, then we must expand our system of identification. One way to do this would be to assign $j_1$ to John and $j_2$ to James. More complex situations require more complex notation.

## 3. A well-defined set

We remark that the concept of set is useful only if we restrict ourselves to sets which are *well defined*. By a well-defined set we mean one whose elements are clearly identified so that there is general (that is, universal) agreement as to whether a given element is or is not a member of the given set.

To clarify this idea we present some examples of sets which are *not* well defined. First,

$$\{\text{the five greatest musical compositions}\}.$$

Clearly this set contains five elements and each element is a musical composition, but beyond this the elements cannot be identified. Even in a small group of people we would have spirited discussion about the identity of the elements. Such arguments and disagreements are not in the province of mathematics.

Another set which is not well defined might be the following:

$$\{\text{the four easiest college courses}\}.$$

Again, the elements of this set cannot be clearly identified in the sense that *everyone* will agree on the same four courses.

On the other hand, the set of right-handed boys or of brown-haired girls in a class are well-defined sets. The pedant may challenge us with Charles who writes right-handed but eats, throws a ball, and bats left-handed and with Shirley whose hair is partly brown and partly something else. We dismiss these questions on the grounds that they are obvious attempts to upset the apple cart. We can get into arguments when we are dealing with pseudo-mathematical examples, that is, when we are using social situations to illustrate mathematical ideas. We do not get into difficulties like this when we are doing genuine mathematics.

Other examples of well-defined sets are

the set whose elements were Presidents of the United States

and

the set whose elements are the counties of Wyoming.

There is no question about the elements of these sets. It is a matter of record that Abraham Lincoln is an element of the first set and William Jennings Bryan is not. It is also true (though not as well known) that Lincoln and Johnson are elements of the second set but Jackson and Garfield are not.[3]


## 4. Universe of discourse

We are getting along quite well in our study of concepts which appear in modern elementary mathematics textbooks. We know what a set is, how to identify its elements, and how to determine if the set is well defined.

For example, given the set of numbers between 3 and 7 which is denoted by {numbers between 3 and 7}, we can answer the questions: does 5 belong to this set? does $3\frac{1}{2}$ belong to this set?—or can we? Suddenly we realize that there is some confusion here. Our first inclination is to say that 5 *does* belong to the set but that $3\frac{1}{2}$ does *not*. On second thought it appears that both numbers belong to the set. Why do we have this indecision when the set seemed to be well defined?

The answer is that we must specify what we are talking about, that is, our **universe of discourse.** If we are talking about natural (that is, counting) numbers, then 5 is an element of the set and $3\frac{1}{2}$ is not. On the other hand, if the universe of discourse consists of *all* numbers and not just the natural numbers, then $3\frac{1}{2}$ *does* belong to the set. Without specifying the universe of discourse, we cannot be sure if the set of numbers between 3 and 7 contains only the three numbers 4, 5, and 6 or infinitely many as in the set

$$\{3.01, 3.02, 3.03, \ldots, 6.99, 3.001, 3.002, \ldots, 6.999, \text{etc.}\}$$

[3] There is no reason why students can't learn other things while they're learning mathematics, especially if they can use the language of mathematics in the process.

We will denote the universe of discourse by $U$ and we will follow the general custom of using capital letters to denote sets.

Note that $U$ is actually a set—an all-inclusive set from among whose members the elements of our various sets will be taken. In the case of the right-handed boys and brown-haired girls, the universe of discourse might be

$$U = \{\text{all children in a classroom}\},$$

that is, the set of all children in a classroom. Such a set $U$ is especially useful in teaching the foregoing ideas to very young children.

If $U$ represents the set of all children in a certain kindergarten classroom, for example, the teacher can form various sets such as

$$\{\text{boys}\}$$
$$\{\text{girls}\}$$
$$\{\text{children wearing something red}\}$$
$$\{\text{children who had eggs for breakfast}\},$$

and so on in great variety. These sets can actually be acted out by the children. The teacher can ask, "Will the set of all children wearing something red please stand?" Following this it can be established why Marcia, for example, is an element of this set and why Keith isn't. Thus, by playing a game, some important ideas can be taught. Learning and teaching of this kind is a pleasurable experience.

## 5. The empty set

It may just happen that, when the teacher asks "Will the set of children who had eggs for breakfast please stand?", no one stands up.[4] It is natural to ask what we can say about a set such as this which has no members. Strange as it seems, the idea of a set with no members *is* quite useful. Such a set is called the **empty set** and is denoted by one of the two symbols

$$\{ \ \} \quad \text{or} \quad \varnothing.$$

The symbol $\varnothing$, read as "the empty set," is much more satisfactory

[4] If this is not the case, the teacher will have no difficulty in asking some other question that will produce a negative response from the entire class.

for denoting the empty set than $\{\ \}$. The latter leads to an incomplete sentence since the braces are read, "the set whose elements are." For example, we write

$$\{b \mid b \text{ is a brown-haired girl}\}$$

which is read, "the set whose elements are b, where b is a brown-haired girl." An equally good way to define this set would be to *list* the brown-haired girls, for example,

$$\{\text{Mary, Patricia, Ruth, Susan, Wilma}\},$$

if these particular girls have brown hair.

We call attention to a common mistake that can be made. Some people feel that the empty set should be denoted by $\{0\}$. This is incorrect because $\{5\}$ consists of the single number five, and $\{0\}$ consists of the single number zero. The empty set has *no elements whatsoever*.

Actually the empty set $\varnothing$ is convenient because it answers many questions that might be raised. For example, $\varnothing$ is the answer to each of the following questions:

1. What is the set of all Presidents of the United States whose last names began with the letter *Z*?
2. What is the set of all natural (counting) numbers between 5 and 6?
3. What is the set of all right triangles that have three equal sides?[5]


## 6. Union of two sets

When we have two sets containing similar elements, we often wish to combine the elements in a single set. We call this process or operation forming the **union** of two sets. The expression "joining two sets" is also used. To form the union of two sets we do just what the word implies. We illustrate with some examples in which we define certain sets of natural numbers, denoted by capital letters. Note that we may assign a capital letter to a set in this section which was used in a different way in some other section. Stated in another way, the letter *B*

[5] We are anticipating somewhat here although this fact is generally known. In Chapter 7 we explain why this is the empty set.

is not restricted to designating the set of brown-haired girls in a class.

Let

$$A = \{9, 6, 3, 10, 14\}$$
$$B = \{4, 5, 8, 7, 6\}.$$

Then the *union* of $A$ and $B$, denoted by $A \cup B$ is defined as follows:

$$A \cup B = \{3, 4, 5, 6, 7, 8, 9, 10, 14\}.$$

Although the operation of forming the union of two sets appears to be simple, there are some important things to notice. First, the sets $A$ and $B$ are well defined even though their elements are not written in natural order. Second, there is no point in repeating the number 6 when we write the elements of $A \cup B$. As soon as we put 6 into the latter we are saying $6 \in A \cup B$. There is no reason to be redundant even though 6 appeared in both $A$ and $B$.

As another example, if

$$C = \{6, 1, 2, 5\}$$

and

$$D = \{1, 2, 3, \ldots, 7\},$$

then

$$C \cup D = \{1, 2, 3, \ldots, 7\} = D.$$

Thus, the union of two sets may be one of the sets. Note that we use the three dots here to mean, "and so on in like fashion" in order to save writing all the numbers.

Again, if

$$U = \{1, 2, 3, 4, \ldots\},$$
$$E = \{2, 4, 6, 8, 10, \ldots\},$$

and

$$F = \{1, 3, 5, 7, 9, \ldots\},$$

then

$$E \cup F = \{1, 2, 3, 4, \ldots\} = U.$$

Here the union of the two sets is the set of natural numbers—our universe of discourse. Note that the set $E$ is the set of *even* numbers and the set $F$ is the set of *odd* numbers, so that when we form the union of $E$ and $F$, we are bound to get *all* the natural numbers. Stated another way, the union of two sets is a set of those elements which belong to one *or* the other of the two sets.

You should be aware of a fundamental difference between sets $D$ and $E$. The set $D$ was designated by using three dots but there was a *last* element, namely, 7. We interpret $D$ as "the set of numbers 1, 2, 3, and so on to (and including) 7." The set $E$ has no last element—the numbers continue indefinitely. We call a set like $D$ a **finite** set and one like $E$ an **infinite** set.

Hence, this leads us into another aspect of sets—the *number of elements* in a set. We will use the notation $n(A)$ to mean, "the number of elements in the set $A$." For the sets mentioned in this section, we have

$$n(A) = 5$$
$$n(B) = 5.$$

Thus we can write

$$n(A) = n(B).$$

We also have

$$n(A \cup B) = 9$$
$$n(C) = 4$$
$$n(D) = 7$$

and so we can also write

$$n(C) < n(D),$$

meaning that the number of elements in the set $C$ *is less than* the number of elements in the set $D$. This fact can also be stated as

$$n(D) > n(C),$$

meaning that the number of elements in the set $D$ *is greater than* the number of elements in the set $C$.

We call attention to a fundamental concept in mathematics—when two numbers $a$ and $b$ are being compared, one and only one of the following three possibilities exist:

$$a < b$$
$$a = b$$
$$a > b.$$

This is known as the **law of trichotomy.**

Finally, we can state a property of the union of sets in terms of the number of its elements. Since $A \cup B$ contains those elements which are either elements of $A$ or elements of $B$, we have

$$n(A) + n(B) \geq n(A \cup B),$$

that is, the sum of the number of elements of sets $A$ and $B$ *is at least as much as* the number of elements in $A \cup B$. The symbol "$\geq$" is read as "is greater than or equal to" and means "is at least as much as."

## 7. Closure

You may recall that in the last section we defined the union of two sets in such a way that the union had the following three properties:

1. The elements in the union could be written in any order as long as all the elements in both sets but no other elements appeared in the union.
2. There was no reason to repeat those elements which appeared in *both* of the constituent sets.
3. The number of elements in the union could not exceed the sum of the number of elements in the constituent sets.

To these properties we add one more. The union of two sets is a *set.* At first glance this seems trivial because one might say, "Of course you get a set when you form the union of two sets! What do you expect to get—a giraffe, an orange crate, a number?" On the basis of limited experience in mathematics we might not see anything remarkable in the fact that the union of two sets is a set. After all, isn't the sum of two natural numbers a natural number? Isn't the product of two natural numbers a natural number? Isn't the quotient of two natural numbers a natural number? The quotients of 12 and 4, of 24 and 3, of 8 and 2, *are* natural numbers, but the quotient of 7 and 2 is *not!* Thus, performing division (and also subtraction) with natural numbers does not *always* result in a natural number. Similarly, there is no good reason to assume a priori that the result of an operation on two sets will be a set.

This brings us to the idea of closure in mathematics. We say a set is **closed** under a certain operation[6] if the result of performing the operation on *any* two members of the set yields another member of the set. When we are talking about sets, that is, when the universe of discourse is *a set of sets*, then we can say that the union of two sets is a set.

We shall see that this concept of closure will help us in Chapter 3 when we discuss geometry. There the closure of sets under the operation of forming the union will help to unify the subject and result in a deeper understanding of it.

## 8. Counting

Coming back to the number of elements in a set, we had no difficulty in determining that

$$n(C) = 4$$

and

$$n(D) = 7,$$

where

$$C = \{6, 1, 2, 5\}$$

and

$$D = \{1, 2, 3, \ldots, 7\}.$$

From this we could easily conclude that

$$n(C) < n(D).$$

But what about the following two sets,

$$E = \{2, 4, 6, 8, 10, \ldots\}$$

and

$$F = \{1, 3, 5, 7, 9, \ldots\}?$$

We recognize that these are *infinite* sets and naturally we are interested

[6] Addition, subtraction, multiplication, division, forming the union, are all called "operations."

in knowing whether the law of trichotomy applies to them. Which of the three possibilities,

$$n(E) < n(F)$$
$$n(E) = n(F)$$
$$n(E) > n(F),$$

holds in the case of infinite sets?

We can arrive at an answer to this question by considering a hypothetical example. Suppose that I work in a hardware store on weekends. The proprietor says to me, "We have some bolts and some nuts but I am not sure how many of each we have. I would like to place an order for one or the other so that we would have the same number of each. Please tell me what to order."

I can attack this problem in one of two ways. One way is to count all the bolts and all the nuts. Suppose that when I do this, I get 258 bolts and 249 nuts. Then I could tell my boss to order 9 nuts so that there would be the same number of bolts as nuts. The second way is to take a bolt out of the bolt barrel and a nut out of the nut barrel, screw the two together and throw the combination into a third barrel. This procedure requires no counting at all—only a *matching*. Note that counting by matching has the advantage that the process is undisturbed by interruptions. When I get through with this job, one of three situations will exist:

1. The bolt barrel will contain some bolts but the nut barrel will be empty.

2. Both the bolt and nut barrels will be empty.

3. The nut barrel will contain some nuts but the bolt barrel will be empty.

In other words, the law of trichotomy again!

Now suppose that the supply of bolts and nuts is infinite like the widow's oil in the Bible. If I can never reach the end of the bolts and nuts but if I can continue to match the bolts and nuts, I must conclude that there are *just as many* bolts as nuts.

This matching of the elements of one set (the bolts) with that of another (the nuts) is called making a **one-to-one correspondence.** If it is possible to make a one-to-one correspondence between the elements of two sets (even though they have an *infinite* number of elements), we must conclude that the two sets have exactly the same number of elements.

Diagrammatically, the two sets $E$ and $F$ can be matched as follows:

$$E = \{2, 4, 6, 8, 10, \ldots, 2n, \ldots\}$$
$$\updownarrow \ \updownarrow \ \updownarrow \ \updownarrow \quad \updownarrow \qquad \updownarrow$$
$$F = \{1, 3, 5, 7, \ 9, \ldots, 2n - 1, \ldots\}.$$

It should be perfectly clear that there can be no element in the set $E$ that does not have a corresponding element in the set $F$ and that, conversely, there can not be an element in the set $F$ which does not correspond to some element in the set $E$. In other words, sets $E$ and $F$ have the *same* number of elements. That is,

$$n(E) = n(F).$$

Using the same argument it can be shown that the sets

$$N = \{1, 2, 3, 4, 5, \ldots, n, \ldots\}$$

and

$$T = \{1000, 2000, 3000, 4000, 5000, \ldots, 1000n, \ldots\}$$

have the same number of elements. Any set that can be put into a one-to-one correspondence with the set of natural numbers $N$ is said to be **denumerable** or **countable.**

## Exercises 1A

1. Name and discuss five reasons for changing the method of teaching mathematics.

2. What four characteristics do the various new mathematics programs have in common?

3. Give an example of a set that is not well defined.

4. Give an example of a set that is well defined.

5. How many elements may a set have?

6. If $A$ is the set of counting numbers which are at least 7 and $B$

is the set of counting numbers which are at most 10, what is $A \cup B$?

7. In exercise 6 what is $n(A)$? $n(B)$? $n(A \cup B)$?

8. If $6 \in E$, what can you say about $E$?

9. Let $U$ be the set of students in your class. If $R = \{$redheaded boys$\}$ and $S = \{$girls wearing red skirts$\}$ what can you say about $R \cup S$? about $R \cup U$? about $S \cup \emptyset$?

10. How can you show that there are as many numbers if you count by ones or by one millions?

11. Given

$$M = \{3, 5, 6, 4, 2, 12\}$$

and

$$T = \{3, 13, 2, 10, 12, 31\},$$

what is $M \cup T$?

12. Explain why it is not possible to have $n(a \cup B) > n(A) + n(B)$.

13. Under what conditions can we have

$$n(A \cup B) = n(A) + n(B)?$$

14. Does $101 \in \{2, 4, 6, 8, 10, \ldots\}$? Why?

15. Is $\{$Olympic champions$\}$ well defined? Why?

16. Give an example of the empty set.

17. Can the universe of discourse contain as few as two elements? If so, give an example.

18. If

$$W = \{7, 6, 23, 5, 2, 4, 1\}$$

and

$$V = \{9, 22, 4, 8, 7, 6\},$$

what is $n(W \cup V)$?

19. In the previous example how does $n(V)$ compare with $n(\emptyset)$?

20. Under what conditions is the union of two sets the empty set?

# 2/The Real Number System (A)

In this chapter we begin the study of the real number system. The term "real" will be made clear in Chapter 10. Until then it will suffice to think of a real number as one that can be represented on a (real) number line such as shown in Figure 2.1. For the present, we will concentrate our attention on some rather special real numbers.

## 1. Natural numbers

It is safe to say that man's earliest experience with numbers was in connection with counting. This bit of history is repeated with each new human being as a child learns to count. The numbers used for counting are called, quite naturally, **counting numbers** or **natural numbers.**

We refer to the totality of these numbers as the set of natural numbers. This set may be designated by the letter $N$ and we can write

$$N = \{1, 2, 3, 4, 5, 6, \ldots\}.$$

Note that we cannot actually count the number of elements in the set $N$ but must say simply that $n(N)$ is *infinite.*

The set $N$ may be visualized by means of a device called a *number line.* This is a line which has marks at equally spaced intervals and these marks are designated 1, 2, 3, 4, etc. Figure 2.1 shows a number line.

We indicate by means of an arrow that the line continues indefinitely to the right.

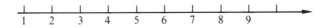

Fig. 2.1  Number Line

Note the resemblance between the above number line and an ordinary ruler. In fact, a ruler is actually a part—a *finite* part—of a number line. Both the ruler and the number line will be valuable aids to us in studying the number system.

## 2. One, the first counting number

The symbol 1 represents the *first* number in the set of natural numbers, the symbol 2 is the *second* number, the symbol 3 the *third* number, and so on. In other words, there is a natural **order** to the natural numbers. In higher mathematics we say that each natural number except one is the **successor** of a preceding number. It is this succession of numbers in order that we call counting.

The number one, however, is not the successor of any natural number. Being the first, it cannot be defined as a successor of anything. Yet the number one is important for we define two as one more than one, three as one more than two, etc. Thus "one" is an all-important number in mathematics, and without it we could not begin to define the set of natural numbers.

## 3. Addition, a binary operation

It is a characteristic of mathematics that a set of numbers by itself is not very useful. We have defined the set $N$ of natural numbers but of what use is it except for counting? In order that the concept of a set of numbers be more useful, we need some *action*; there must be some interplay between the numbers.

Such interplay is accomplished by a mathematical **operation**. Basic among operations is **addition** since it can be thought of in terms of counting. Thinking of the natural numbers as they would appear on a number line, we describe addition as counting to the *right*. Thus we say that the sum of 3 and 4 is 7 because we can start at 3 on the number line, count 4 to the right and this brings us to 7. In symbols,

$$3 + 4 = 7.$$

The operation of addition is indicated by the plus $(+)$ sign. Addition is a **binary** operation meaning that a *single* number results when the operation is applied to *two* numbers called **addends.** In other words, a binary operation, such as addition, produces one number where two existed before. Note carefully that addition is defined only for *two* numbers. The significance of this will become apparent in Section 6 of this chapter.

We call attention to the meaning of the equality in $3 + 4 = 7$. This means that the *same* number can be expressed in two different ways. We call 3, 4, and 7 **numerals**—they *represent* numbers. These same three numbers may be represented in other ways, for example, by III, IV, and VII, or by the words, "three," "four," and "seven," or by the words "trois," "quatre," and "sept," and so forth. Thus we emphasize the fact that a number has many names. In "$3 + 4 = 7$" we indicate that the number seven can be expressed as $3 + 4$ or equivalently as 7.

## 4. Closure

Very early in the game we realize that when we add two natural numbers we again get a natural number. The situation is similar to the one we encountered in Section 7 of Chapter 1. There we discussed another binary operation—forming the union of two sets—and indicated that the result of forming the union was again a set. This phenomenon is known as **closure.** We say that the set of natural numbers is closed under the operation of addition. This means that if *any* two natural numbers are added the result will always be a natural number.

That the natural numbers are closed under the operation of addition follows as a consequence of two things. First, we described addition as counting to the right and, second, the number of natural numbers is infinite. No matter where we start and no matter how far we count to the right, we will always end up with a natural number. For example,

$$1\ 000\ 000 + 1\ 000 = 1\ 001\ 000,$$

a natural number;

$$1\ 000\ 000\ 000 + 1\ 000\ 000 = 1\ 001\ 000\ 000,$$

a natural number, and so forth.

The concept of closure is a fundamental one in mathematics. In fact, the real number system will be developed on the basis of requirements imposed that a set be closed under various operations.

We summarize the above and state property **A1** of the natural numbers under addition.

**A1.** If $a$ and $b$ are any two elements of the set $N$, then $a + b$ is an element of $N$ (closure property). Stated in words, the sum of two natural numbers is always a natural number.

## 5. Commutative property of addition

Further examination of the set $N$ of natural numbers and the operation of addition (or counting to the right) reveals another fact. We notice that whether we start with 3 on a number line and add 4 or start with 4 and add 3, we arrive at 7. That this is no mere coincidence is shown by the fact that $5 + 1$ and $1 + 5$ are both 6, $5 + 10$ and $10 + 5$ are both 15, etc.

The reader is encouraged to try some additions on a number line, first starting with one addend and then the other. Pupils, of course, should also make many investigations of the two ways of performing addition.

In all of the above investigations it will be found that if $a$ and $b$ are any two natural numbers whatever, then $a + b$ and $b + a$ are the *same* number. No one can find a single exception to this! But neither can anyone check all the possibilities in order to be certain that the order in which two natural numbers is added is immaterial. It is intuitively acceptable but not capable of being proved.

To say that $a + b$ and $b + a$ express the same number, we may write

$$a + b = b + a.$$

This is known as the **commutative** property of the natural numbers under the operation of addition. A person commutes if he goes back and forth. We speak of commuting students as those who go back and forth between home and college each day. The sum $a + b$ expresses the idea in one way and the sum $b + a$ expresses it in a *reverse* way. Thus it is natural to call the property

$$a + b = b + a,$$

the commutative property.

We say that the natural numbers have the commutative property under addition or, equivalently, the natural numbers commute under addition.

This can be stated as the second property of the natural numbers under addition and summarized as follows:

**A2.** If $a$ and $b$ are any two elements of the set $N$ then

$$a + b = b + a$$

(commutative property).

Stated in words, the order in which two natural numbers are added is immaterial.


## 6. Associative property of addition

Now we come to one of the most perplexing problems in elementary mathematics. It is impossible to add three numbers simultaneously! This may come as a shock to the reader who hasn't thought about this, but it is, nevertheless, true. If you doubt it, try to add 3, 4, and 8 all at once. In other words, try to perform "instant addition" with these three numbers.

You may say, "I can look at those numbers and immediately respond with 15." If you analyze your thought processes carefully, however, you will find that you did one of several things. Either you added 3 and 4, then added the resulting 7 to 8, or you added 4 and 8, then added the resulting 12 to 3, or you added 8 and 3, then added the resulting 11 to 4. In no case did you add more than two numbers at a time.

This, of course, makes sense because, after all, addition was defined as a binary operation. This means that only *two* numbers can be added at a time.

If it is necessary to add *three* numbers, say $a$, $b$, and $c$, then we may proceed in one of two [1] ways. We may add $a$ and $b$ and add $c$ to the sum or we may add the sum of $b$ and $c$ to $a$. The first way may be designated as $(a + b) + c$. We use parentheses to indicate that we are talking about a *single* number, namely, the sum of $a$ and $b$. The second way may be designated by $a + (b + c)$.

Again we can check many cases, that is, we can assign various counting numbers to $a$, $b$, and $c$ and verify that

$$(a + b) + c = a + (b + c).$$

We cannot, however, hope to check the validity of this relationship for *all* counting numbers. We assume that this property of addition holds for all counting numbers. We call it

**A3.** If $a$, $b$, and $c$ are any three elements of the set $N$, then

$$(a + b) + c = a + (b + c)$$

(associative property).

In other words, when three counting numbers are to be added, pairs may be grouped (or *associated*) in any manner whatever.

It is, of course, possible to find the sum $a + b + c$ by adding $a$ and $c$ and then adding $b$ to this sum. When we do this, we are actually using the commutative property of addition followed by the associative property. In other words,

$$a + (b + c) = a + (c + b) \quad \text{by } \mathbf{A2,}$$
$$= (a + c) + b \quad \text{by } \mathbf{A3.}$$

When there are more than three addends we can use the associative property to reduce the problem to cases already considered. For example,

$$a + b + c + d = (a + b) + (c + d)$$
$$a + b + c + d + e = (a + b) + (c + d + e).$$

## 7. Subtraction, the inverse of addition

With the advent of the space age "countdowns" or "counting back-

[1] If you feel that there are more than two ways to add three numbers, please be patient and your question will be answered shortly.

ward" became fashionable. On a number line counting backward would mean counting to the *left*. This process "undoes" what addition does, hence it is called the **inverse** of addition or **subtraction.**

Every addition fact has a corresponding inverse or subtraction fact. For example, the addition fact

$$6 + 3 = 9$$

has the inverse

$$9 - 3 = 6.$$

Note how the order of the three numerals, 6, 3, and 9 has been exactly reversed or inverted in the two statements. It is natural, therefore, to call addition and subtraction inverse operations, that is, subtraction is the inverse of addition and addition is the inverse of subtraction.

Because of the close relationship between addition and subtraction, it is recommended that these two processes be taught concurrently. At the time the child learns to read

$$4 + 3 = 7$$

as "four plus three is seven," he should also learn to read

$$7 - 3 = 4$$

as "seven minus three is four." The symbol "+" is read "plus" and indicates the operation of addition, while the symbol "−" is read "minus" and indicates the operation of subtraction.

We designated the commutative property of addition of natural numbers by **A2.** By this property we can write

$$4 + 3 = 7$$

as

$$3 + 4 = 7.$$

The inverse of the first is

$$7 - 3 = 4,$$

and of the second,

$$7 - 4 = 3.$$

Thus each addition fact actually leads to two subtraction facts.

**The Real Number System (A)**

It is interesting to note that *none* of the three properties of addition of natural numbers holds for subtraction. Property **A1** (closure property) stated that the sum of any two natural numbers was another natural number. While the difference of many natural numbers *is* another natural number ($12 - 8 = 4$, $6 - 5 = 1$, $10 - 8 = 2$, etc.), the fact that $2 - 4$ is *not* a natural number prevents us from extending property **A1** to subtraction.

Property **A2** (commutative property) stated that the order in which two natural numbers is added is immaterial. The order in subtraction, however, is of prime importance; $8 - 4$ is not the same thing at all as $4 - 8$.[2]

Finally, property **A3** (associative property) stated that if three natural numbers were to be added they could be grouped in pairs in any manner. It was necessary to consider pairs because addition was a binary operation. Subtraction is also a binary operation but the associative property fails to hold as shown by the single example: $(8 - 4) - 2$ is 2, while $8 - (4 - 2)$ is 6.

## 8. Multiplication, a binary operation

Addition of like addends can be easily simplified. If we were confronted with

$$3 + 3 + 3 + 3 + 3,$$

we would naturally think of this as the sum of *five* addends, each of which is *three*. A brief way of writing this is

$$5 \times 3,$$

that is "five times three" or "the product of five and three." The operation indicated by the symbol "$\times$" is called **multiplication.** We can think of $a \times b$ as the sum of $a$ addends, each of which is equal to $b$.

This way of looking at multiplication as "repeated addition" is convenient and is recommended for dealing with natural numbers in the

[2] In this connection we recommend that the teacher say, "we do not *now* have a number for $4 - 8$ to represent," rather than categorically stating, "you can't subtract 8 from 4." The former makes the existence of negative numbers an open question while the latter denies their existence.

primary grades. Later, in Chapter 9, we will look at a more sophisticated concept of multiplication.

Multiplication is also a binary operation because we apply it to *two* numbers to obtain a *single* number. In an indicated product like $5 \times 3$ the second numeral tells us what the equal addends are and the first numeral tells us how many of these addends there are. Thus

$$5 \times 3 = 3 + 3 + 3 + 3 + 3,$$

and the result is, of course, 15 since we already know how to add.

The process of multiplication can be easily illustrated on a number line. In the above example we would start at 3 and make four jumps of three each to the right in order to arrive at 15. We call 15 the **product** of 5 and 3 and write

$$5 \times 3 = 15.$$

Because multiplication is actually counting to the right, that is, addition, it follows that the product of any two natural numbers is again a natural number. In other words, the natural numbers are **closed** under the operation of multiplication. We state this as property

**M1.** The product of any two natural numbers is a natural number (closure property).

We mention again that it is not possible to check the closure property by finding the products of all possible pairs of natural numbers. It is something that we must take for granted.

## 9. Commutative property of multiplication

Notice how each new topic that we consider uses some facts discussed in previous sections. It is this building-block character of mathematics that forces us to build a firm foundation in the elementary grades. To do this we must also keep our eye on what will happen in future grades. One can hardly start laying bricks unless he has some idea of what the finished product will be. It is a characteristic of modern mathematics teaching that the teacher cannot just "stay a day ahead of the class."

We have already checked by means of a number line (or by using our knowledge of addition facts) that

$$5 \times 3 = 3 + 3 + 3 + 3 + 3 = 15.$$

Now we look at the product $3 \times 5$. By definition, this is the same as

$$5 + 5 + 5 = 15.$$

We can check a number of products and we will invariably find that the *order* in which multiplication of two natural numbers is performed is immaterial. We call this the commutative property of the natural numbers under the operation of multiplication. Thus we have

**M2.** If $a$ and $b$ are any two natural numbers, then

$$a \times b = b \times a$$

(commutative property).

In the past, teachers of arithmetic have not taken full advantage of this property. They have not sufficiently stressed the fact that if a child "forgets" the product $6 \times 9$, he may remember the product $9 \times 6$. Because of individual differences it is easier to learn and remember some multiplication facts than others. An awareness of the fact that multiplication of natural numbers is commutative leads to

**Table 2.1**  Multiplication of Natural Numbers

| × | 1 | 2 | 3 | 4 | 5 | 6 | 7 | 8 | 9 | 10 |
|---|---|---|---|---|---|---|---|---|---|----|
| 1 | 1 | 2 | 3 | 4 | 5 | 6 | 7 | 8 | 9 | 10 |
| 2 | 2 | 4 | 6 | 8 | 10 | 12 | 14 | 16 | 18 | 20 |
| 3 | 3 | 6 | 9 | 12 | 15 | 18 | 21 | 24 | 27 | 30 |
| 4 | 4 | 8 | 12 | 16 | 20 | 24 | 28 | 32 | 36 | 40 |
| 5 | 5 | 10 | 15 | 20 | 25 | 30 | 35 | 40 | 45 | 50 |
| 6 | 6 | 12 | 18 | 24 | 30 | 36 | 42 | 48 | 54 | 60 |
| 7 | 7 | 14 | 21 | 28 | 35 | 42 | 49 | 56 | 63 | 70 |
| 8 | 8 | 16 | 24 | 32 | 40 | 48 | 56 | 64 | 72 | 80 |
| 9 | 9 | 18 | 27 | 36 | 45 | 54 | 63 | 72 | 81 | 90 |
| 10 | 10 | 20 | 30 | 40 | 50 | 60 | 70 | 80 | 90 | 100 |

the necessity for memorizing fewer multiplication facts. This can be illustrated by examining the multiplication Table 2.1.

In Table 2.1 we call the dotted line the "main diagonal." Note that, except for the numbers along the main diagonal, all numbers in the table occur twice. This means that it would be possible to memorize all the entries by memorizing the numbers on and above the main diagonal and remembering the commutative property.

We mention also that the numbers along the main diagonal of Table 2.1 are called **perfect squares.** The significance of this term will be made clear in Chapter 4.

## 10. Associative property of multiplication

Just as in the case of addition, we are faced with the problem of how to multiply three natural numbers in view of the fact that multiplication is a binary operation. In other words, what is

$$2 \times 3 \times 5?$$

There is no way to obtain the product of three numbers instantaneously. When we analyze our thought processes, we realize that either we multiplied 2 by 3 and multiplied the result by 5 or else we multiplied 3 by 5 and then multiplied this result by 2. In both cases we arrived at the number 30 as the final result.

The two different methods used can be illustrated by the following:

$$(2 \times 3) \times 5 \text{ and } 2 \times (3 \times 5).$$

In both cases the result is 30 and, if we examine a great many products of three numbers, we are forced to the conclusion that

$$(a \times b) \times c = a \times (b \times c)$$

for any natural numbers $a$, $b$, and $c$, whatever. Again, we cannot possibly check the above equality for all natural numbers, but we *assume* it is true for all. We call this property the **associative** property of the natural numbers under multiplication and state

**M3.** If $a$, $b$, and $c$ are any natural numbers whatever, then

$$(a \times b) \times c = a \times (b \times c)$$

(associative property).

We call attention to the fact that the product $2 \times 3 \times 5$ can also be evaluated by saying, "$2 \times 5 = 10$ and $10 \times 3 = 30$." This presupposes an intermediate step, namely,

$$2 \times (3 \times 5) = 2 \times (5 \times 3),$$

using the commutative property **M2**.

Thus we have properties **M1**, **M2**, and **M3** of the natural numbers under multiplication analogous to properties **A1**, **A2**, and **A3** under addition. There is one additional property, however, for multiplication which so far does not have its counterpart for addition. This property is discussed in the next section.

## 11. One, the multiplicative identity

Using the definition that multiplication is repeated addition, we have

$$3 \times 5 = 5 + 5 + 5 = 15$$
$$2 \times 5 = 5 + 5 \quad\quad = 10,$$

but what can we say about $1 \times 5$? We define it to be 5, that is, $1 \times 5 = 5$. We can generalize the last statement and say

$$1 \times a = a$$

for *every* natural number $a$.

This property of one under multiplication will turn out to be one of the most useful properties of the number system. We will use this idea repeatedly in our later work.

We call one the **multiplicative identity** because no matter which natural number is multiplied by one, it remains unchanged. We state

**M4.** For any natural number $a$,

$$1 \times a = a \times 1 = a.$$

The intermediate step comes about because of property **M2** (commutative property).

We stress the fact that in this chapter we are studying the various properties of the set of natural numbers under certain operations. This study is essential to our later work because every step in an arithmetic problem will be justified, that is, each step will be explained by one of the properties of the number system under consideration.

## 12. Distributive property of multiplication over addition

Now that we have presented the binary operations of addition and multiplication and have discussed some of the properties of each, the question naturally arises as to what procedure to follow when both operations are present. In order to have both addition and multiplication, we need to consider a minimum of three natural numbers. For example, we might consider

$$2 \times 3 + 6$$

or

$$2 + 3 \times 6.$$

As we look at the above two examples we realize that there is some uncertainty involved. Do we interpret $2 \times 3 + 6$ as $6 + 6$ or as $2 \times 9$? Do we interpret $2 + 3 \times 6$ as $5 \times 6$ or as $2 + 18$? Since each interpretation produces a different result, it is obvious that we need to have some understanding about the symbols. For this reason we use parentheses [3] to make the meaning clear. If we intend $2 \times 3 + 6$ to mean $2 \times 9$, we will write

$$2 \times (3 + 6).$$

Placing parentheses around the sum $3 + 6$ means that we wish to consider the single number 9. Hence, $2 \times (3 + 6)$ becomes $2 \times 9$ or 18. There is certainly nothing remarkable about this. When we notice, however, that $(2 \times 3) + (2 \times 6)$ also produces 18, we have food for thought! Is it a coincidence that

$$2 \times (3 + 6) = (2 \times 3) + (2 \times 6)?$$

We can try other natural numbers, for example,

$$4 \times (5 + 2) = 4 \times 7 = 28$$

[3] We call attention to the fact that in the "old" mathematics parentheses were usually not introduced until ninth grade algebra.

and
$$4 \times (5 + 2) = (4 \times 5) + (4 \times 2) = 28,$$
and also
$$1 \times (6 + 9) = 1 \times 15 = 15$$
and
$$1 \times (6 + 9) = (1 \times 6) + (1 \times 9) = 15.$$

A number of examples will convince us that what is happening here is no coincidence but is a result of the properties of the natural numbers. We have, in fact, uncovered another property of the natural numbers called the **distributive property.** We state

**D.** For any three natural numbers $a$, $b$, and $c$,
$$a \times (b + c) = (a \times b) + (a \times c).$$

It is also true that
$$(b + c) \times a = (b \times a) + (c \times a) = (a \times b) + (a \times c)$$

because of the commutative property of multiplication of natural numbers.

The word "distributive" comes from the fact that in
$$3 \times (5 + 7)$$

we *distribute* the multiplication over the addition. In other words, we write
$$3 \times (5 + 7) = (3 \times 5) + (3 \times 7).$$

The multiplication by 3 has been applied to *both* addends—it has been *distributed* over the 5 and the 7.

The distributive property will also be used quite often later. For example, we will say that $2/3 + 5/3 = 7/3$ because
$$2/3 + 5/3 = 1/3 \times (2 + 5) = 1/3 \times 7 = 7/3,$$

and not because "only like things can be added."

## 13. One-to-one correspondence

We return to an idea that was touched upon briefly in Section 8 of

Chapter 1, namely, *counting*. We have been talking about the set of counting numbers and its properties. We can designate this set by

$$N = \{1, 2, 3, 4, 5, 6, \ldots\}.$$

The set $N$ is called an *infinite* set, meaning that it has an infinite number of elements. There are many other sets, of course, which have an infinite number of elements. Following are some examples:

$$A = \{2, 5, 8, 11, 14, \ldots\}$$
$$B = \{4, 8, 12, 16, 20, \ldots\}.$$

It is possible to match the elements of the sets $A$ and $B$ with the elements of $N$. Moreover, this matching can be done in a one-to-one manner. This means, for example, that to each element of set $A$ there corresponds an element of set $N$ and that each element of set $N$ is the "correspondent" of an element of set $A$.

When the elements of a set can be matched in a one-to-one manner with the elements of $N$, we say that the set is **countable** or **denumerable**. In the above examples sets $A$ and $B$ are denumerable sets.

## 14. Arithmetic using the properties of counting numbers

We are now ready to examine how the processes of arithmetic can be carried out. Always we keep in mind the properties of the counting numbers and use these as our guidelines. Never do we perform operations which cannot be justified on the basis of the properties discussed in the previous sections.

Eventually many arithmetic processes become automatic but the purpose of modern mathematics teaching is to instil understanding, not automation. At any time the pupil should be able to give a logical explanation of a method he uses, if he is challenged.

There are not too many changes in teaching addition. Mainly we want to keep in mind the commutative and associative properties of addition. The first has to do with the order of the addends, the second with the grouping of the addends. In essence, natural numbers may be added in any order and grouped in any way.

Offhand these seem to be well-known ideas. But herein lies one of the aspects of the "new mathematics." In teaching addition we have an opportunity to cater to individual differences. Students are different—let's face it! No matter how thoroughly we drill the addition facts, there will be students who recognize $8 + 7$ but hesitate on $7 + 8$. There will be those who immediately see the combination $4 + 9 + 6$ and those who recognize $8 + 5 + 7$ more easily. Of course there will always be those who recognize various combinations with equal ease - more power to them!

The point is that requiring students to add columns of numbers in order and to check the results by adding in the reverse order is not in agreement with modern philosophy. This type of training does *not* take into account the commutative and associative properties of addition and can result only in making of mathematics a despised chore. No teacher wants to do this!

Thus in teaching addition we allow the students as much freedom as possible. We drill $8 + 9$ as much as $9 + 8$ (maybe more), but we realize that after we're through there will be those who hesitate when confronted with $8 + 9$ but not when presented with $9 + 8$. Who cares?—the commutative property takes care of things.

We begin the study of addition of two-digit numbers by doing this *horizontally* using the associative and commutative laws. This may seem like the difficult way but it builds strong foundations and affords excellent drill. We illustrate with a number of examples.

$$27 + 8 = (20 + 7) + 8 = 20 + (7 + 8)$$
$$= 20 + 15 = 35$$
$$8 + 19 = 8 + (10 + 9) = (8 + 9) + 10 = 17 + 10 = 27$$
$$36 + 45 = (30 + 6) + (40 + 5) = (30 + 40) + (6 + 5)$$
$$= 70 + 11 = 81$$
$$426 + 17 = (400 + 20 + 6) + (10 + 7)$$
$$= 400 + (20 + 10) + (6 + 7)$$
$$= 400 + 30 + 13$$
$$= 430 + (10 + 3)$$
$$= 440 + 3 = 443.$$

Notice how we can add quite well before it's necessary to say anything about "carry." This is desirable because the concept of carrying is a little more sophisticated than that of addition. After the students can handle horizontal addition well, we introduce vertical addition. This can be done by looking at the previous examples in another way.

For instance,

| 27 | 8 | 36 | 426 |
|---|---|---|---|
| + 8 | +19 | +45 | + 17 |
| 15 | 17 | 11 | 13 |
| +20 | +10 | +70 | 30 |
| 35 | 27 | 81 | +400 |
| | | | 443. |

In this work, of course, it is *mandatory* that place value be kept in mind at all times. When adding 36 and 45, we add 6 and 5 to get 11—the first 1 represents ten, the second, one. Then we add 30 and 40 to get 70 and write the 70 correctly with respect to the 11. We use correct language—we do *not* say "3 and 4" when we mean "30 and 40." The use of sloppy terminology will only make everything horribly confused later.

All the "old" methods of teaching addition—lining up corresponding place values, speed, accuracy, etc.—are still important today and always will be. The "newness" is mostly in the attitude the teacher has and in the attitude he wants the students to have. In brief—efficiency instead of drudgery!

It is a characteristic of mathematics that inverse operations are often much more difficult than the operations themselves.[4] For example, subtraction is more difficult than addition, division is more difficult than multiplication and finding the square root is more difficult than squaring. Perhaps the main reason for this is that teachers have "glorified" the inverse operation unnecessarily. If subtraction is taught *at the same time* as addition, it will lose much of its mystery. When we teach the addition fact $3 + 4 = 7$, we can also teach the subtraction facts $7 - 4 = 3$ and $7 - 3 = 4$ (because of the commutative property which states $3 + 4 = 4 + 3$).

Note how the *inverse* operation is truly an inverse one. In one case we have

$$3 + 4 = 7$$
$$\longrightarrow$$

and in the other,

$$7 - 4 = 3.$$
$$\longleftarrow$$

[4] Kovach, Ladis D.: "Unilateral Mathematics Teaching," *Math. Teacher* (56), no. 7, pp. 550-552, November 1963.

We have *reversed the order* of the numbers and also replaced $+$ by its inverse $-$. A thorough understanding of the process at this stage will make division (and other inverse processes) much simpler later.

We pursue this idea as far as we can—even with two-digit numbers. For example, the inverse of $7 + 5 = 12$ is $12 - 5 = 7$, the inverse of $5 + 7 = 12$ is $12 - 7 = 5$, etc. Always we're making use of the commutative property and the idea of inverse operations.

How do we teach $17 - 9$? There are two equally good methods. In one we stress that $17 - 9 = \Box$ means $\Box + 9 = 17$ and the unknown $\Box$ must be filled with 8. The other method is based on something that we should be stressing all along, namely, that a number has *many* names. One way to write 9 is $5 + 4$ so that $17 - (5 + 4)$ becomes $(10 + 7) - (5 + 4)$. This can be written

$$
\begin{array}{c}
10 + 7 \\
-(5 + 4) \\
\hline
5 + 3
\end{array}
\quad \text{or} \quad
\begin{array}{c}
10 + 7 \\
-(4 + 5) \\
\hline
6 + 2
\end{array}
$$

and we obtain 8 in both cases. Note that the use of parentheses is essential. At all times we retain the same *number* within the parentheses—only its form is changed. Changing the form of a number is called "renaming" or "regrouping" and takes the place of the time-honored (?) "borrowing."

In teaching subtraction it may be advisable to use the vertical form much sooner than in the case of addition. We illustrate with some of the varieties that are possible.

$$
\begin{array}{c}
24 \\
-\ 6 \\
\hline
\phantom{10 + 8}
\end{array}
\quad
\begin{array}{c}
10 + 14 \\
-\ \ \ \ \ \ 6 \\
\hline
10 + \ 8 \text{ or } 18
\end{array}
\quad
\begin{array}{c}
10 + 14 \\
-\ 6 \\
\hline
4 + 14 \text{ or } 18
\end{array}
\quad
\begin{array}{c}
18 + 6 \\
-\ \ \ \ \ \ 6 \\
\hline
18 + 0 \text{ or } 18.
\end{array}
$$

Once again we are catering to individual differences automatically! One student may feel more secure with the second method, for example, while an unusually bright student will look for combinations like the last one.

It is undoubtedly true that there is less agreement among educators and mathematicians regarding the best way to teach subtraction than anything else. Either we have not yet found the *ideal* way or there are a number of methods equally good. We tend to favor the latter view. What may work well with one group of students may not work well with another. In any event the teacher should be familiar with many methods of teaching subtraction. In this connection see also Chapter 5 where removing a subset from a set is presented as another way of teaching subtraction.

After the students learn their multiplication tables (Notice that it is not possible to eliminate rote learning entirely!) they are ready to begin multiplication of two-digit numbers. This again is done horizontally, using the distributive law. We give some examples.

$$18 \times 7 = (10 + 8) \times 7 = (10 \times 7) + (8 \times 7)$$
$$= 70 + 56 = 126$$
$$6 \times 29 = 6 \times (20 + 9) = (6 \times 20) + (6 \times 9)$$
$$= 120 + 54$$
$$= 174$$
$$12 \times 16 = (10 + 2) \times (10 + 6)$$
$$= (10 \times 10) + (10 \times 6) + (2 \times 10) + (2 \times 6)$$
$$= 100 + 60 + 20 + 12$$
$$= 192.$$

We don't do too much horizontal multiplying of two-digit numbers by two-digit numbers—only enough to give the student an appreciation for the vertical form. After the horizontal method has been mastered, we consider the vertical form. The previous examples now appear as follows:

$$
\begin{array}{ccc}
18 & 6 & 12 \\
\times\,7 & \times 29 & 16 \\
\hline
56 & 54 & 12 \\
70 & 120 & 60 \\
\hline
126 & 174 & 20 \\
& & 100 \\
\hline
& & 192.
\end{array}
$$

Note that in the early stages vertical multiplication contains more partial products than will be necessary later. This is merely another example of the philosophy that it is better to teach the "short cuts" *after* there is an understanding of the basic ideas. The latter involves careful attention to place value, for example. In multiplying 18 by 7 we say, "8 × 7 is 56, 10 × 7 is 70." In multiplying 6 by 29 we say, "9 × 6 is 54, 20 × 6 is 120." In multiplying 12 by 16 we say, "6 × 2 is 12, 6 × 10 is 60, 10 × 2 is 20, 10 × 10 is 100." We always use the properties of the number system with which we are working.

It is important to note that the above method of teaching multiplication requires a knowledge of multiplication by multiples[5] of 10, 100, 1000, etc. This knowledge is most easily acquired by extending the drill of the multiplication facts to include multiples of 100 as well as of 10.

At the time that we are teaching $9 \times 6 = 54$, we also point out that the inverse of this is $54 \div 6 = 9$. Because of the commutative property of multiplication, $9 \times 6 = 54$ can also be written $6 \times 9 = 54$ and the inverse of this is $54 \div 9 = 6$. Thus we introduce division as the inverse of multiplication.

As we consider more complicated problems, it is necessary to think of division as *repeated subtraction* (since multiplication is *repeated addition*). In a very elementary manner this means that $24 \div 6 = 4$ because we can subtract 6 from 24 successively until we reach zero. For example,

$$
\begin{array}{r}
24 \\
-\ 6 \\
\hline
18 \\
-\ 6 \\
\hline
12 \\
-\ 6 \\
\hline
6 \\
-\ 6 \\
\hline
0.
\end{array}
$$

Thus $24 \div 6 = 4$ because we have subtracted six *four* times. Similarly, $22 \div 6$ is 3 with a remainder of 4 as shown by the following:

$$
\begin{array}{r}
22 \\
-\ 6 \\
\hline
16 \\
-\ 6 \\
\hline
10 \\
-\ 6 \\
\hline
4.
\end{array}
$$

[5] A multiple of 10 is a counting number times 10. Thus 20, 30, 60, 90, etc. are multiples of 10; 100, 400, 700, etc. are multiples of 100. See Chapter 8.

Here we have subtracted six *three* times and are left with a remainder of 4.

In order to save time, we don't subtract the *divisor* but rather we subtract *multiples* of the divisor. This leads into the process known as "long division." We again illustrate with some examples.

$$
\begin{array}{r|l}
23 \,\big|\, 369 & \\
\phantom{23\,\big|\,}230 & 10 \\
\hline
\phantom{23\,\big|\,}139 & \\
\phantom{23\,\big|\,}115 & 5 \\
\hline
\phantom{23\,\big|\,}24 & \\
\phantom{23\,\big|\,}23 & 1 \\
\hline
\phantom{23\,\big|\,}1 & \\
\end{array}
$$

The reasoning here goes as follows, "What multiple of 23 can we subtract from 369?" An *easy* answer is 10, hence 230 is subtracted at a crack. Now we are left with 139 and our previous multiple of 10 is halved giving us 115 or $5 \times 23$. When we subtract this, we are left with 24 and the final subtraction follows readily. We add up the multiples of 23 we have subtracted and they add to 16. Thus the answer to the division problem is 16 and there is a *remainder* of 1.

Consider the division problem $897 \div 29 = $ . We can keep the form of this problem intact and perform the division. It is only necessary to keep the multiples of the divisor lined up properly both vertically and horizontally. For example,

$$
\begin{array}{ll}
897 \div 29 = 30\tfrac{27}{29}. & \\
\phantom{897 \div 2}290 & 10 \\
\hline
\phantom{897 \div 2}607 & \\
\phantom{897 \div 2}290 & 10 \\
\hline
\phantom{897 \div 2}317 & \\
\phantom{897 \div 2}290 & 10 \\
\hline
\phantom{897 \div 2}27 & \\
\end{array}
$$

We have demonstrated here the approach that might be used by a timid student or one who did not have much confidence in his ability to handle divisors ending in 9.

Another, more difficult example:

$$9675 \div 276 = \underline{35 \ \text{R} \ 15.}$$

$$
\begin{array}{ll}
8280 & 30 \\
\hline
1395 & \\
1380 & 5 \\
\hline
15 &
\end{array}
$$

Finally, using the old format:

$$
\begin{array}{r|l}
106 \ | \ 51783 & \\
10600 & 100 \\
\hline
41183 & \\
\cancel{42400} & \cancel{400} \\
31800 & 300 \\
\hline
9383 & \\
\cancel{9540} & \cancel{90} \\
8480 & 80 \\
\hline
903 & \\
848 & 8 \\
\hline
55 &
\end{array}
$$

We have 488 for the quotient and a remainder of 55. Here we have demonstrated the recommended procedure to be used when wrong guesses are made. They are simply ruled out and the work proceeds. Not only are the figures available for later use to help make estimates but the paper remains neater than if many erasures had been made.

We have outlined the methods by which the arithmetic operations are taught. At each successive grade level refinements are made to the processes of multiplication and division. In the former we make use of the property of numbers that $a + 0 = a$. This property is called A4 and discussed in Chapter 6. Hence

$$
\begin{array}{ccc}
12 & & 12 \\
\times \ 16 & & \times \ 16 \\
\hline
12 & \text{becomes} & 12 \\
60 & & 6 \\
20 & & 2 \\
100 & & 1 \\
\hline
192 & & 192
\end{array}
$$

since the addition of zeros doesn't change the sum. Omitting the zeros allows us to compress the work and we also perform one of the additions mentally. In the end the problem has the following appearance:

$$\begin{array}{r} 12 \\ \times\ 16 \\ \hline 72 \\ 12 \\ \hline 192. \end{array}$$

It seems like we got to Farmer Murphy's barn by the long way, but there is less hocus-pocus in the new method. We can justify, explain, defend, understand each step on the basis of the properties of the number system.

In the case of division we must proceed more slowly because the job is more difficult. Our aim is to find multiples of the divisor which are not necessarily multiples of 10 or 100. In other words to subtract the *maximum* multiple of the divisor at each step of the process. This, too, will look like the long division of the old school when we get through.

Teachers (and students) who have been taught by these modern methods are enthusiastic about them. It is already apparent that both the weak and the strong students can benefit greatly.

## 15. Mathematics is a game

We call attention to the fact that mathematics has many of the characteristics of a game. An essential part of a game are the pieces, as in chess and checkers. So far our pieces have been sets and the natural (or counting) numbers.

Pieces without some kind of action, however, cannot be called a game. In mathematics the action is designated by a symbol ($\cup$, $+$, $-$, $\times$, $\div$, for example) and called an operation. To form the union of two sets requires that the elements of the two sets be joined in one set. To find the sum of 3 and 5 requires that one start at 3 and count 5 to the right. Thus each operation is a call to action of a certain type.

Pieces and action still do not constitute a game until some rules are laid down. The rules are an essential part of a game in that they govern the action. In one game, for example, it is entirely proper to move straight ahead (chess) while in another game only diagonal movement is permitted (checkers).

In mathematics the rules are given by the definitions and by the basic properties (or axioms) of the particular system with which we are dealing. When forming the union of two sets we do not repeat elements which the two sets have in common; multiplication of a number by one does not change the number, etc.

Finally, it should be mentioned that mathematics is an honest game, meaning that everyone follows the rules. Failure to do so may result in poor grades or dismissal from class. Replacing $5 \times 7$ with $5 + 7$ or $8 \times 7$ with 52 are violations of the rules.

## Exercises 2A

1. Which of the following are natural numbers: $4 + 6$, $4 \div 6$, $4 \times 6$, $4 - 6$?

2. Why can't we define the number one as "one more than zero?"

3. How many different properties of the natural numbers are used in determining that $27 \times 9 = 243$?

4. Is the set of multiples of 10 closed under addition? Explain.

5. Analyze the reasoning of the pupil who attacks the problem $27 - 19$ by regrouping 27 as $19 + 8$.

6. Criticize the following argument: Since $1 \div 1 = 1$, $4 \div 2 = 2$, $12 \div 4 = 3$, $20 \div 5 = 4$, the set $N$ of natural numbers is closed under the operation of division.

7. Prove that the commutative property does not apply to natural numbers when the operation is subtraction.

8. Does the associative property hold for the natural numbers when the operation is subtraction? Explain.

9. The distributive property has to do with the operations of multiplication and addition. If they are replaced by their inverses, division and subtraction, does the distributive property still hold?

10. Show by a single example that the natural numbers in general do not commute under the operation of division.

11. Explain why the number one is the identity for division as well as for multiplication.

12. Perform the following additions by looking for familiar combinations:

(a) 17
    29
    43

(b) 82
    19
    38

(c) 165
    92
    108

(d) 36
    48
    94

(e) 47
    94
    68

13. Repeat exercise 12 and use different combinations.

14. Repeat exercise 12 and perform the additions without using the concept of "carrying."

15. Perform the following subtractions by renaming where necessary:

(a)  36
    −27

(b)  92
    −59

(c) 102
    −87

(d) 113
    −76

(e) 100
    −69

Hint: Both numbers may be renamed.

16. Repeat exercise 15 by renaming in a different manner.

17. Perform the following multiplications horizontally using the distributive property:

(a) $16 \times 7$   (b) $39 \times 8$   (c) $9 \times 62$   (d) $27 \times 6$
(e) $89 \times 8$   (f) $36 \times 24$.

18. Repeat exercise 17 by doing the multiplications vertically still using the distributive property.

19. Perform the following divisions by the method outlined in Section 14:

(a) $367 \div 28$      (b)  $92 \div 17$      (c)  $861 \div 106$
(d) $902 \div 69$      (e) $1893 \div 67$      (f) $3967 \div 493$.

20. Write the inverses of each of the following:

(a) $19 + 7 = 26$         (b) $65 \times 8 = 520$
(c) $39 - 16 = 23$         (d) $1073 \div 37 = 29$.

21. Show that the sets in Section 13 can be matched in the following way:

(a) to each $n \in N$ there is an element $(3n - 1) \in A$.
(b) to each $n \in N$ what is the corresponding element in $B$?

# 3/Geometry (A)

## 1. A point undefined

The geometry that can be included in the mathematics at the elementary level is called informal or *intuitive* geometry. As the name implies, this is a kind of geometry in which we appeal to the intuition of the pupils. We make this appeal in lieu of giving formal proofs. The pupils see a large number of special cases and from these they draw certain generalizations. This process is also called *inductive* reasoning.

We believe that this is the proper first contact a child should have with geometry. We further believe that this contact should come as early as possible. Professor Patrick Suppes of Stanford University and his colleagues have taught intuitive geometry to first and second graders with great success.[1] Many educators are of the opinion that there is an advantage to introducing some mathematical topics in earlier grades than was formerly done. It seems that in the past we have been guilty of "selling our pupils short"; they can understand and appreciate much more advanced mathematics than we ever thought.

In studying the number system we found that the number one could not be defined. It was the number with which we constructed the whole natural number system. In geometry a point is a fundamental idea. It cannot be defined; it cannot be seen; it exists only in the mind. Admittedly we are getting into some difficult concepts here. It must be kept in mind, however, that all of mathematics exists only in the mind. We can see the symbols that represent numbers, for example, but the numbers themselves are abstract concepts.

[1] Hawley, Newton, and Patrick Suppes: "Geometry for Primary Grades," Books 1 and 2, Holden-Day, San Francisco, 1961.

An effective way for the teacher to introduce the concept of a point is to hold up his pencil and say to the class, "Please look at the tip of the point of my pencil. Do not take your eyes away from it no matter what I do with the pencil. Even if I remove the pencil, keep your eyes fixed on the place where the point of the pencil *was*." When the pupils have concentrated on the tip of the pencil for several seconds, the teacher puts the pencil back in his pocket and says, "You are now looking at a *point*."

The class gets the idea that a point is just a *position* and that a dot on the paper or a blob of chalk on the chalkboard is merely a representation (a crude one at that) of a point. A little playacting as described above is much more effective than saying that a point has no size.

If a point exists only in the mind, and, if in geometry we study sets of points, it can be readily seen that geometry itself exists only in the mind. This certainly explains why some mathematicians, notably Leonhard Euler (1707–1783) and L. Pontrjagin (1908–    ), have done outstanding work though they were blind.


## 2. Lines are sets

We need points to describe another geometrical figure—a line. A **line** is a *set of points*. But more than this, a line is a set consisting of an infinite number of points, and extending infinitely in two opposite directions. An example of a line is the number line on which we can show both positive and negative numbers. In Figure 3.1 are shown some lines which are designated $L_1$, $L_2$, and $L_3$:

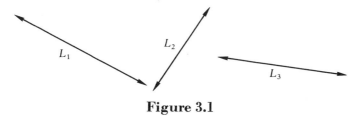

**Figure 3.1**

It is more convenient to select two points on a line, label them, and refer to the line in this way. Using this notation, we refer in Figure 3.2 to the line $\overleftrightarrow{AB}$:

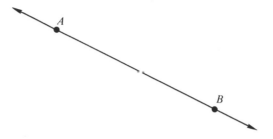

**Figure 3.2**

We call attention to the fact that in the elementary school a line is taken as undefined also. We cannot use the old (but incorrect!) definition, namely, "a line is the shortest distance between two points" because we have not yet defined "distance." There should be no difficulty about lines, however, since this notion is very familiar to children.

In some cases we do not wish to consider a *whole* line. This was the case when we used a number line to show the natural numbers. If we wish to go only in one direction, we have the **ray** $\overrightarrow{AB}$ (Fig. 3.3). We

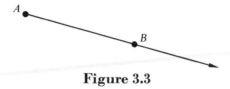

**Figure 3.3**

call $A$ the **end-point** of the ray $\overrightarrow{AB}$.

Finally, we may not wish to consider lines which are as indefinite as $\overleftrightarrow{AB}$ or $\overrightarrow{AB}$. We may be interested only in a portion of the line. We designate such a portion $\overline{AB}$ and call it a **line segment.** Figure 3.4 pictures such a line segment. Now we have two end-points, $A$ and $B$.

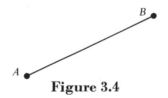

**Figure 3.4**

Since lines are sets of points, lines can't be seen because they have no width or thickness. We can, however, represent a line by a pencil line or a chalk line. Such a visible representation is properly called a "picture of a line" or a "representation of a line." This distinction is usually not made and, following general custom, we refer to both a line and its representation as a "line."

In summary, the geometry of the line—called *one-dimensional* geometry—includes the study of lines, rays, and line segments. A line is determined by any two distinct points on it. For example, $\overleftrightarrow{AB}$, $\overleftrightarrow{BA}$, $\overleftrightarrow{CA}$, $\overleftrightarrow{AC}$, $\overleftrightarrow{BC}$, $\overleftrightarrow{CB}$ are different designations for the line shown in Figure 3.5. Similarly, $\overrightarrow{EF}$ and $\overrightarrow{EG}$ are different designations for the

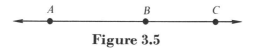

**Figure 3.5**

ray shown in Figure 3.6. Finally, the line segment shown in Figure

**Figure 3.6**

3.7 may be designated either as $\overline{MN}$ or $\overline{NM}$. From the last example

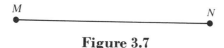

**Figure 3.7**

of the line segment it can be seen that the two points $M$ and $N$ completely determine the line segment. There is no way to designate this line segment without using both the letters $M$ and $N$, that is, without specifying the end-points. Hence we say, "a line segment is determined by two points" rather than "a line is determined by two points." Language is an important part of modern mathematics teaching.

## 3. Planes that can't be seen

Traditionally, a plane has been defined as a level or flat surface. This is really not a definition since "flat surface" is a synonym for "plane." Fortunately, we have enough mathematical concepts at our disposal now to enable us to develop the concept of a plane.

Consider a line such as $\overleftrightarrow{AB}$ and a point $C$ not on this line. Figure 3.8 illustrates the situation as it would appear on a chalkboard. Now

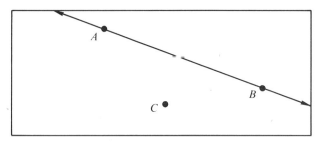

**Figure 3.8**

draw all possible lines that can be drawn between any pairs of points. Note that as soon as we draw a line, such as $\overleftrightarrow{AC}$, for example, we can also connect various points of $\overleftrightarrow{AC}$ with points of $\overleftrightarrow{AB}$. Colored chalk is quite effective for drawing a great number of these lines. After a while the chalkboard will have the appearance shown in Figure 3.9 where the dotted lines represent colored ones.

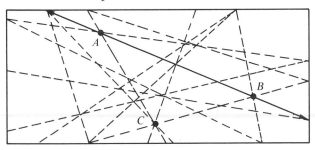

**Figure 3.9**

This, of course, is just a very small number of the "all possible" lines that can be drawn between any two points. Here is where we need our imagination to furnish the rest of the lines. It can be seen without much difficulty that every point on the chalkboard will eventually have a line through it.

We can now define a *plane*. In the above process we started with a line $\overleftrightarrow{AB}$ and a point $C$ not on this line. Then we considered all possible lines joining pairs of points. Thinking of each line as a set of points, a **plane** is the union of all the possible lines.

It is most effective to use colored chalk, say red, to draw the many lines shown in the last figure. Then, when the class sees the hopelessness of drawing all possible lines, the chalk may be held broadside and a portion of the chalkboard can thus be colored red.

We call attention to the fact that our picture of a plane is very incomplete. The limitations of the blackboard did not permit us to draw complete lines but only portions of them. Imagining each line to be infinite in extent we can also imagine the infinite extent of a plane.

Sometimes we wish to consider only a part of a plane. The points of the plane lying above the line $\overleftrightarrow{AB}$ of the last example constitute a **half-plane**. The points of the plane lying below the line $\overleftrightarrow{AB}$ also constitute a half-plane.

When dealing with lines and planes we are actually considering sets of points—sets which have an infinite number of elements. Because of the infinite nature of these sets the word "half" does not have the usual meaning here. For example, any point of a line divides the line into two rays. Similarly, any line in a plane divides the plane into two half-planes.

We can restrict our discussion of planes even further by considering a part of a plane such as a chalkboard or a desk top. These are called plane **regions** and will be studied further in Chapter 7.

The study of planes and of plane regions belongs to *two-dimensional* geometry. On a line we could only go back and forth on the line and we called this one-dimensional geometry. In a plane we can not only go back and forth on a line but we can move off the line also, hence planes belong to two-dimensional geometry.

## 4. Space that can't be drawn

A very neat definition of (physical) space is the following: Space is the set of all points. Since a point has no size but merely specifies a location, the set of all points takes into account the entire universe. Clearly, there are points inside the earth, inside a piece of chalk, and everywhere in the vastness between the stars.

The common notion of space is that of "empty space" but the idea we need in geometry is different from this. Points, being locations, are simply everywhere and when we say, "the set of all points" is "space," we mean both *empty* and *occupied* space.

Another way to develop the idea of space is to begin with a plane and a point not in the plane.[2] If we again draw all possible lines between

[2] Note the analogy between "a plane and a point not in the plane" and "a line and a point not on the line" used in the last section.

arbitrary pairs of points, we will have an infinity of lines. The union of these lines (again considered as sets of points) is space.

This development can be done in the classroom but it requires an active imagination on the part of the pupil and an even more active demonstration by the teacher. This is how the lesson might be given: "We know what a plane is and that it is infinite in extent. We can consider this chalkboard as a very small portion of a plane. As I stand here in front of the chalkboard and hold up this piece of chalk, you may think of the tip of the chalk as a point which is not in the plane of the chalkboard. Now draw a line through some point in the chalkboard and the tip of my chalk. This line can be drawn only in imagination although we could represent the line by a string attached to the chalkboard and to my chalk. Remember that a line extends infinitely so that we have the line extending into the room and out the opposite wall and on across the street and so on. We also have it extending behind the chalkboard into the next classroom, through their chalkboard, into the school yard and on and on. Now take another point in the chalkboard and draw a line through it and the tip of my chalk. Continue this process until you have used every point in the chalkboard. Then draw lines between the points of the lines running through the room. After *all possible* lines are drawn, take the union of these lines—this union is what we call space."

The reader may now appreciate the words "space that can't be drawn" at the beginning of this section. Our pictorial representations of space figures become necessarily more crude as we try to transfer them to the plane of the chalkboard or the paper. Try to represent a ball, for example. This is one of the simplest of space figures, yet without some knowledge of shading, it is not possible to make a reasonably faithful drawing.

The study of space belongs to *three-dimensional* geometry. In three dimensions we can move not only back and forth (as on a line) and off the line (as on a plane) but also off the plane. In fact, there is no limitation to the direction in which we can move in three dimensions.

## 5. Measure and length

In order to introduce the concept of measure, we return to one-

dimensional geometry and line segments. Suppose we have a line
segment such as $\overline{AB}$ in Figure 3.10. Before we can find the measure

**Figure 3.10**

of this segment we need a *unit of measure*. Since we are going to find
the measure of a line segment, it seems reasonable that our unit of
measure should also be a line segment. Let $\overline{MN}$ be a unit of measure
shown in Figure 3.11.

**Figure 3.11**

Finding the **measure** of $\overline{AB}$ consists of determining how many
times we have to use the unit of measure $\overline{MN}$ in order to completely
"cover" $\overline{AB}$. We may cut $\overline{MN}$ out of paper, for example, and actually
place one end on $A$, mark the other end, move to this new point, and
repeat the process. It is permissible to cut $\overline{MN}$ in two or three or
whatever part is necessary to do the measuring as accurately as possible.
In the above example the unit of measure $\overline{MN}$ fits on $\overline{AB}$ exactly
$3\frac{1}{2}$ times.

We say, "the measure of $\overline{AB}$ is $3\frac{1}{2}$." Note that the measure of a
line segment is a *number*. Moreover, this number depends on the particular unit of measure being used. In order to standardize the process
of measurement, names have been given to various standard units of
measure: inch, foot, yard, mile, light year, [3] centimeter, meter, kilo-
meter, etc.

The unit of measure $\overline{MN}$ of the last example is the inch. We have
already determined that the measure of $\overline{AB}$ is $3\frac{1}{2}$ using this particular
unit of measure. We can now say also that the **length** of $\overline{AB}$ is $3\frac{1}{2}$
inches. We call attention to the fact that two things are involved in

[3] The distance light, traveling at 186 000 miles per second, travels
in one year.

specifying length. First, the measure (using a unit of measure) and second, the name of the unit of measure.

Note that we measure only line segments in one-dimensional geometry since the measure of a line or of a ray is infinite. In measuring we keep in mind that whatever we measure and the unit of measure are both the same geometric configurations. This idea will be expanded upon in Chapter 7.

## Exercises 3A

1. Using the idea of one-to-one correspondence, show that there are as many points on a short line segment as on a longer one.

2.

   (a) Designate the line shown.

   (b) Designate the ray having end-point at $R$ and containing point $S$.

   (c) Designate the ray having end-point at $T$ and containing point $R$.

   (d) What is the union of the two rays in (b) and (c)?

   (e) Designate the line segment having end-points at $R$ and $S$.

   (f) Does $T$ lie on the line segment described in (e)?

3. Consider the line shown in exercise 2. Consider also all possible lines parallel to this one which can be drawn on this page. What is the union of all these lines?

4. The line shown in exercise 2 divides the plane of this page into two half-planes. What is the union of these half-planes if the line is assumed to be in one of the half-planes?

5. What might be studied in zero-dimensional geometry? Explain.

6. Under what conditions is the measure of a line segment zero?

7. Using the following unit of measure (transferred to a piece of paper) find the measure of the indicated segments:

$$\vdash\!\!-\!\!-\!\!-\!\!-\!\!-\!\!-\!\!-\!\!\dashv$$

Unit of Measure

   (a) $\overline{FG}$ of Section 2

(b) $\overline{GE}$ of Section 2

(c) $\overline{EF}$ of Section 2

(d) $\overline{FE}$ of Section 2

(e) $\overline{AB}$ of Section 3

(f) $\overline{AC}$ of Section 3

(g) $\overline{CB}$ of Section 3

(h) Verify that the sum of the measures of $\overline{AC}$ and $\overline{CB}$ exceeds the measure of $\overline{AB}$ in Section 3.

(i) Under what conditions would the sum in (h) not exceed the measure of $\overline{AB}$?

# 4/Number Theory (A)

## 1. Primes and composites

Number theory is a branch of algebra which in turn is a branch of mathematics. In some branches of number theory we work with the set $N$ of natural numbers exclusively. Hence it is appropriate that topics from number theory be introduced in the early grades. This may require a change in our thinking since not too many years ago number theory was studied by sophomore or junior mathematics majors in college. Of course the student's first contact with number theory in the elementary school cannot be compared to the college course as far as method or content are concerned. The fact remains, however, that many concepts considered as advanced a few years ago have filtered down into the elementary mathematics program. This is one reason that the "new" mathematics seems so strange to many.

We begin by examining the natural numbers with a view to how they can be obtained by multiplication of other natural numbers. The work is most conveniently presented in the form of a table such as in Table 4.1:

### Table 4.1

$1 = 1 \times 1$

$2 = 1 \times 2$

$3 = 1 \times 3$

$4 = 1 \times 4 \ = 2 \times 2$

$5 = 1 \times 5$

$6 = 1 \times 6 \ = 2 \times 3$

$7 = 1 \times 7$

$8 = 1 \times 8 \ = 2 \times 4$

$9 = 1 \times 9 \ = 3 \times 3$

$10 = 1 \times 10 = 2 \times 5$

$11 = 1 \times 11$

$12 = 1 \times 12 = 2 \times 6 = 3 \times 4$

$13 = 1 \times 13$

$14 = 1 \times 14 = 2 \times 7$

$15 = 1 \times 15 = 3 \times 5$

$16 = 1 \times 16 = 2 \times 8 = 4 \times 4$

$17 = 1 \times 17$

$18 = 1 \times 18 = 2 \times 9 = 3 \times 6$

$19 = 1 \times 19$

We are now ready to make a number of observations. First, we note that the table does not contain unnecessary duplications. For example, 6 can be written as $6 \times 1$ and as $3 \times 2$ in addition to the forms shown in the table. These, however, follow from the commutative property of the natural numbers under multiplication.

Next we note that *every* natural number can be expressed as a product. This is due to the fact that every natural number can be written as one (the multiplicative identity) times the number.

Starting with 2 we see that some numbers can be written *only* as one times the number. These numbers are 2, 3, 5, 7, 11, 13, 17, and 19 and are called **primes.** Specifically these are the first eight prime numbers in order. By convention, we do not call 1 a prime. Those numbers which are not prime are called **composites.** The first ten composite numbers in order are 4, 6, 8, 9, 10, 12, 14, 15, 16, and 18.

We observe further that 2 is the only even prime, all the others being odd numbers. Finally, we note that in some cases two prime numbers are as close to each other as they can get, being separated by one even number. This occurs in the pair 5 and 7; in 11 and 13; in 17 and 19. These are called **twin primes** and they have been extensively studied.

A method for finding prime numbers is known as the "sieve of Eratosthenes." Eratosthenes was a Greek mathematician who lived about 230 B. C. Hence prime numbers have interested mathematicians for some time.

## 2. Factoring, using trees and exponents

The process of writing a number as a product of two other numbers is called **factoring.** We say, for example, that 2 and 3 are **factors** of 6 since $6 = 2 \times 3$. We also say that prime numbers can only be factored *trivially*, meaning that a prime number has only two factors—one and itself.

The Fundamental Theorem of Arithmetic states that every number can be expressed as a product of prime factors in a unique way. Since $3 \times 4 = 12$, we call 3 and 4 *factors* of 12. In fact, the number 12 has 6 factors—1, 2, 3, 4, 6, and 12. Again, the first and last of these are trivial factors, hence we shall confine our attention to the factors

**Number Theory (A)**                                                      **65**

2, 3, 4, and 6. Of these four factors only 2 and 3 are prime. The other two, however, can be expressed as $2 \times 2$ and $2 \times 3$, respectively. In other words, we can factor 12 in two ways:

$$12 = 3 \times 4 = 3 \times 2 \times 2$$
$$12 = 2 \times 6 = 2 \times 2 \times 3.$$

Notice that both factorizations, when continued until primes are obtained, are the same except for order. The commutative property under multiplication establishes the uniqueness stated by the Fundamental Theorem.

Let us factor some numbers into prime factors. Note that only composite numbers can be so factored.

$$8 = 2 \times 4 = 2 \times 2 \times 2$$
$$10 = 2 \times 5$$
$$14 = 2 \times 7$$
$$18 = 3 \times 6 = 3 \times 2 \times 3$$
$$20 = 10 \times 2 = 2 \times 5 \times 2$$
$$24 = 6 \times 4 = 3 \times 2 \times 2 \times 2$$
$$32 = 8 \times 4 = 2 \times 2 \times 2 \times 2 \times 2$$
$$36 = 9 \times 4 = 3 \times 3 \times 2 \times 2$$
$$54 = 9 \times 6 = 3 \times 3 \times 2 \times 3.$$

Factoring at the elementary level can also be conveniently done by using *factor trees*. We illustrate by exhibiting factor trees for factoring 45 and 72.

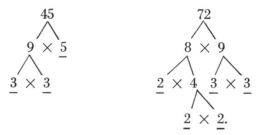

A number has been factored into its prime factors when it is no longer possible to add "branches." The final result is a product of the numbers underlined in the above factor trees. Because of the Fundamental Theorem of Arithmetic it doesn't matter how the intermediate steps are taken—the end result will always be the same.

We illustrate by presenting various factor trees for 1890. In every

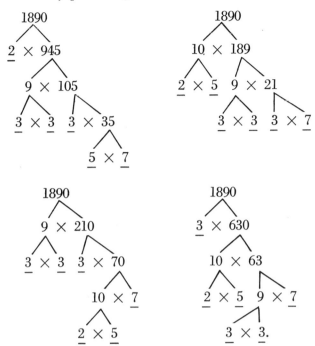

case we have underlined the prime factors of 1890.

Looking at the ends of the branches of the above factor trees we can pick out the prime factors of the number. We can then express the number as a product of its prime factors. Following are some examples:

$$45 = 3 \times 3 \times 5$$
$$72 = 2 \times 2 \times 2 \times 3 \times 3$$
$$1890 = 2 \times 3 \times 3 \times 3 \times 5 \times 7.$$

It can be seen that, when the same prime factor is repeated a number of times, the expression of a number as a product of its prime factors can become quite long. This is especially true for numbers like the following:

$$64 = 2 \times 2 \times 2 \times 2 \times 2 \times 2$$
$$648 = 2 \times 2 \times 2 \times 3 \times 3 \times 3 \times 3$$
$$1125 = 3 \times 3 \times 5 \times 5 \times 5.$$

Thus it is desirable to have a more simplified system of notation. Such a system is called *exponent notation*. In this system we indicate with a superscript—called an **exponent**—how many times a number is to be taken as a factor. For example,

$$3^5 \text{ means } 3 \times 3 \times 3 \times 3 \times 3$$
$$3^4 \text{ means } 3 \times 3 \times 3 \times 3$$
$$3^3 \text{ means } 3 \times 3 \times 3$$
$$3^2 \text{ means } 3 \times 3$$
$$3^1 \text{ means } 3.$$

In each case we have used the same number, 3, called the **base** and applied different exponents to it. The number $3^4$ is read either as "three with an exponent four" or "three to the fourth power" or "three to the fourth."

Using exponent notation we can rewrite some of the previous prime factorizations as follows:

$$8 = 2^3$$
$$18 = 2 \times 3^2$$
$$20 = 2^2 \times 5$$
$$24 = 2^3 \times 3$$
$$32 = 2^5$$
$$36 = 2^2 \times 3^2$$
$$45 = 3^2 \times 5$$
$$54 = 2 \times 3^3$$
$$64 = 2^6$$
$$72 = 2^3 \times 3^2$$
$$648 = 2^3 \times 3^4$$
$$1125 = 3^2 \times 5^3$$
$$1890 = 2 \times 3^3 \times 5 \times 7.$$

It can be seen that exponents provide a way of expressing large numbers with less writing. In this sense exponents are a kind of "mathematical shorthand." Today's scientific age requires the use of large numbers, so that exponents are especially useful. We can write 100 000 000 000 miles as $10^{11}$ miles and \$1 000 000 000 as $10^9$ dollars.

## 3. The decimal system of numeration—base 10

Today, in all but a few isolated and uncivilized parts of the world, the *decimal* system of numeration is used.

By the decimal system of numeration we mean a number system based on *ten*. It is generally supposed that this is due to man's anatomical characteristic of having ten fingers. There are two features of a number system based on ten. One is that ten digits namely,[1] 0, 1, 2, 3, 4, 5, 6, 7, 8, 9, are used and the other is that we use a *place value* system in which each place has a value ten times as great as the place to its right. To write any numeral, for example 6743, we use only the digits above and put these in various positions to obtain various values. The digit 3 is in the *ones* place, the 4 is in the *tens* place, the 7 is in the *hundreds* place, and the 6 is in the *thousands* place.

All of this means that 6743 can be decomposed into a sum as follows:

$$6743 = (6 \times 1000) + (7 \times 100) + (4 \times 10) + (3 \times 1).$$

Using exponent notation, this sum can be written as

$$6743 = (6 \times 10^3) + (7 \times 10^2) + (4 \times 10) + (3 \times 1).$$

We say that 6743 has been written in **expanded notation**. *Any* number can be expressed in a similar fashion. We give some examples.

$$39 = (3 \times 10) + (9 \times 1)$$
$$406 = (4 \times 10^2) + (0 \times 10) + (6 \times 1)$$
$$3\,971 = (3 \times 10^3) + (9 \times 10^2) + (7 \times 10) + (1 \times 1)$$
$$86\,073 = (8 \times 10^4) + (6 \times 10^3) + (0 \times 10^2) + (7 \times 10) + (3 \times 1).$$

We should be fully aware of the place values at all times but especially in counting. Since 9 is the last digit in the decimal system of numeration, the number after 9 must be written by using the previous digits. The next number is 10 which means one ten and zero ones. Similarly, after 19 we write 20, that is, two tens and zero ones. After 99 we write 100, that is, one hundred, zero tens, and zero ones. Note how zero invariably follows nine in counting and that simultaneously the number in the place at the left is increased by one.

All of this must be perfectly understood. Without this understanding other systems of numeration will seem mysterious and difficult.

[1] We have not yet formally introduced zero, and will not do so until Chapter 6, but this should cause no difficulty at this point.

## 4. The quinary system of numeration—base 5

There are a number of perfectly valid reasons for considering systems of numeration other than the decimal. We list some of these for the reader's information:

1. Other systems of numeration are being used today. Systems based on 2 and 8 are used in electronic computers. Systems based on 5 and 20 are used by certain primitive tribes.

2. Learning about other systems of numeration gives the student a greater insight into the decimal system.

3. Working in other systems of numeration is fun and yet it also provides valuable drill.

4. Other systems of numeration are used in certain higher branches of mathematics to prove various theorems.

If the decimal system of numeration became popular because man has ten fingers, it is natural to consider, as a first departure from this, a system based on five. This system is called the **quinary system.**

As a matter of fact, some tribes in the New Hebrides use a quinary system[2] in which they count as follows: *tai* (1), *lua* (2), *tolu* (3), *vari* (4), *lima* (5—this word also means "hand" in their language), *o tai* (6, that is, other one), *o lua* (7—other 2), *o tolu* (8—other 3), *o vari* (9—other 4), and *lua lima* (10—that is, two hands). A reasonable conjecture for the use of this peculiar kind of system can be made if one realizes that the land occupied by these people abounds in unfriendly wild animals and even more unfriendly savages. This situation makes it mandatory that a man carry a spear at all times for protection and this, of course, leaves only *one* hand for counting purposes.

In the quinary system of numeration we use only *five* digits, namely,

$$0, 1, 2, 3, 4.$$

Moreover, the place values in this system are such that each place has a value which is *five* times that of the place to its right.

A typical numeral in the quinary system would be 324, meaning 3 twenty-fives, 2 fives and 4 ones. The numeral 42 means 4 fives and 2 ones. In order to prevent confusing them with numerals in the decimal system, we write them as $(324)_5$ and $(42)_5$. The latter is read, "four

[2] See Dubisch, Roy: "The Nature of Number," The Ronald Press, New York, 1952.

two in base five." It would be incorrect to read this as "forty-two in the base five" since the word "forty" means "four tens" and not "four fives" as is meant in this case. Similarly, the word "hundred" means "ten times ten" so that the 3 in $(324)_5$ represents three "five times fives" and cannot be read as "three hundred."

There *are* words in our language for "four fives" and for "five times fives" so that we could read $(42)_5$ as twenty-two, that is, 4 fives and 2 ones. We could also read $(324)_5$ as "three twenty-fives, two fives and four ones" but "three two four to the base 5" is much simpler.

We need to know the place values in the quinary system. They are, reading from right to left, ones, fives, twenty-fives, one hundred twenty-fives, six hundred twenty-fives, and so on. Thus we can write

$$(324)_5 = (3 \times 25) + (2 \times 5) + (4 \times 1)$$

or

$$(324)_5 = (3 \times 5^2) + (2 \times 5) + (4 \times 1),$$

using exponent notation. If we wish, we may evaluate the quantity on the right side of the last expression to obtain

$$(3 \times 5^2) + (2 \times 5) + (4 \times 1) = 75 + 10 + 4 = 89.$$

In other words, 324 in the quinary system corresponds to 89 in the decimal system and vice versa. We write

$$(324)_5 = (89)_{10}.$$

Note that all of the arithmetic necessary to make a conversion from one system to another is done in the familiar decimal system. This provides valuable drill which is done eagerly by pupils because they have been motivated by a new situation.

We give some more examples of converting from the quinary to the decimal system.

$$
\begin{aligned}
(1043)_5 &= (1 \times 5^3) + (0 \times 5^2) + (4 \times 5) + (3 \times 1) \\
&= (1 \times 125) + (0 \times 25) + (4 \times 5) + (3 \times 1) \\
&= 125 + 0 + 20 + 3 \\
&= (148)_{10} \\
(300)_5 &= (3 \times 5^2) + (0 \times 5) + (0 \times 1) \\
&= (3 \times 25) + 0 + 0 \\
&= (75)_{10}
\end{aligned}
$$

$$(24321)_5 = (2 \times 5^4) + (4 \times 5^3) + (3 \times 5^2) + (2 \times 5) + (1 \times 1)$$
$$= (2 \times 625) + (4 \times 125) + (3 \times 25) + (2 \times 5) + (1 \times 1)$$
$$= 1250 + 500 + 75 + 10 + 1$$
$$= (1836)_{10}.$$

In every case it requires more digits to represent the number in the quinary system than it does in the decimal system. This, of course, is due to the fact that the place values in the quinary system are less than they are in the decimal system.

We are now ready to convert from the decimal to the quinary system. Before we begin, it might be well to write down some of the place values in the quinary system:

$$3125, \ 625, \ 125, \ 25, \ 5, \ 1.$$

Let us start with 978 which is clearly in the decimal system. (Why?) This number certainly does not contain any 3125's but it does contain one 625. Putting a one in the 625's place still leaves 353 unaccounted for. (Why?) Now putting a two in the 125's place takes care of all but 103 of the 353. (Why?) A four in the 25's place and a three in the one's place will complete the job. We must be careful, however, to put a zero in the five's place also. (Why?) In summary, we can write $(978)_{10}$ as follows:

$$(978)_{10} = (1 \times 625) + (2 \times 125) + (4 \times 25) + (0 \times 5) + (3 \times 1)$$
$$= (12403)_5.$$

In Chapter 8 we will show how this computation can be done in a more systematic manner.

Let us see how to count in the quinary system so that we can learn to do arithmetic in base five. For comparison we list the numbers in the decimal system with the corresponding numbers in base five in Table 4.2.

### Table 4.2

| Decimal | 0 | 1 | 2 | 3 | 4 | 5 | 6 | 7 | 8 | 9 | 10 | 11 | 12 | 13 |
|---|---|---|---|---|---|---|---|---|---|---|---|---|---|---|
| Quinary | 0 | 1 | 2 | 3 | 4 | 10 | 11 | 12 | 13 | 14 | 20 | 21 | 22 | 23 |

| Decimal | 14 | 15 | 16 | 17 | 18 | 19 | 20 | 21 | 22 | 23 | 24 | 25 | 26 | 27 | 28 |
|---|---|---|---|---|---|---|---|---|---|---|---|---|---|---|---|
| Quinary | 24 | 30 | 31 | 32 | 33 | 34 | 40 | 41 | 42 | 43 | 44 | 100 | 101 | 102 | 103 |

We note that 18 in the decimal system is above 33 in the quinary. The latter means three fives and three ones and this, of course, is the same as 18. Decimal 28 corresponds to quinary 103 since the latter indicates one in the twenty-five's place and three in the one's place for a total of 28.

In order to do arithmetic in the base five system, it is convenient to have addition and multiplication tables. (Tables 4.3 and 4.4).

<table>
<tr><td colspan="6" align="center">**Table 4.3**</td><td colspan="6" align="center">**Table 4.4**</td></tr>
<tr><td>+</td><td>0</td><td>1</td><td>2</td><td>3</td><td>4</td><td>×</td><td>0</td><td>1</td><td>2</td><td>3</td><td>4</td></tr>
<tr><td>0</td><td>0</td><td>1</td><td>2</td><td>3</td><td>4</td><td>0</td><td>0</td><td>0</td><td>0</td><td>0</td><td>0</td></tr>
<tr><td>1</td><td>1</td><td>2</td><td>3</td><td>4</td><td>10</td><td>1</td><td>0</td><td>1</td><td>2</td><td>3</td><td>4</td></tr>
<tr><td>2</td><td>2</td><td>3</td><td>4</td><td>10</td><td>11</td><td>2</td><td>0</td><td>2</td><td>4</td><td>11</td><td>13</td></tr>
<tr><td>3</td><td>3</td><td>4</td><td>10</td><td>11</td><td>12</td><td>3</td><td>0</td><td>3</td><td>11</td><td>14</td><td>22</td></tr>
<tr><td>4</td><td>4</td><td>10</td><td>11</td><td>12</td><td>13</td><td>4</td><td>0</td><td>4</td><td>13</td><td>22</td><td>31</td></tr>
</table>

We call attention to several features of these tables. In both tables the first row is the same as the first column, the second row is the same as the second column, etc. This symmetry is due to the fact that addition and multiplication are both commutative.

The entries in the table can be found by counting in base five or by using the following type of reasoning. To find $4 + 4$, we say, $4 + 4$ is 8 and 8 can be expressed as 1 five and 3 ones or 13 in base 5. To find $4 \times 4$, we say $4 \times 4$ is 16 and 16 can be expressed as 3 fives and 1 one or 31 in base 5.

Note that the addition table can also be used for subtraction since they are inverse operations. To find $12 - 3$ means we are looking for a number $N$ such that $N + 3 = 12$. From the addition table it can be seen that $N = 4$, that is $12 - 3 = 4$.

In a similar manner the multiplication table can be used for division since these are also inverse operations. To find $11 \div 3$ is the same as finding a number $N$ such that $N \times 3 = 11$. From the multiplication table we find that $N = 2$, that is $11 \div 3 = 2$. This makes sense as long as we remember not to say, "eleven divided by three is two." We say instead, "In base five, one one divided by three is two."

## 5. The Roman system of numeration

We are now able to appreciate the number system used by the Romans. The basic symbols in the Roman system are

$$I, V, X, L, C, D, M.$$

Each number is either five times or two times the previous one, with the five and two alternating. For example V is five times I, X is two times V, L is five times X, C is two times L, etc.

The place value of the Roman system was quite complicated. For example, IX was 9, XI was 11, XII was 12, and IIX was meaningless. We can begin to understand the difficulties that the Romans faced when we look at partial addition and multiplication tables. (Tables 4.5 and 4.6).

| Table 4.5 | | | | | | Table 4.6 | | | | |
|---|---|---|---|---|---|---|---|---|---|---|
| + | I | II | III | IV | V | × | I | II | III | IV | V |
| I | II | III | IV | V | VI | I | I | II | III | IV | V |
| II | III | IV | V | VI | VII | II | II | IV | VI | VIII | X |
| III | IV | V | VI | VII | VIII | III | III | VI | IX | XII | XV |
| IV | V | VI | VII | VIII | IX | IV | IV | VIII | XII | XVI | XX |
| V | VI | VII | VIII | IX | X | V | V | X | XV | XX | XXV |

The reader is invited to try his hand at subtraction and division with the aid of the above tables. We can readily appreciate the answer a student gave to the question, "What advantages does the Roman system of numeration have?" He said, "The Roman numerals are useful on buildings where it is easier to make straight lines; V is easier to make than 5." We certainly cannot argue with his answer.

### Exercises 4A

1. List all prime numbers less than 100.

2. List all twin primes less than 100.

3. What are the prime factors of the following numbers?

(a) 81, (b) 441, (c) 100, (d) 225, (e) 1 000 000.

4. How many prime numbers are there between 101 and 150? What are they?

5. How many composite numbers are there between 150 and 200? What are they?

**6.** Is 263 prime or composite?

**7.** Make factor trees for the following numbers:
   (a) 150, (b) 720, (c) 1800, (d) 735.

**8.** Write the number represented by each of the following:
   (a) $4^3 \times 3$, (b) $2^2 \times 3^3$, (c) $2^2 \times 3^2 \times 5^2$, (d) $7^3 \times 2^4$.

**9.** Write 39 605 as a sum using powers of 10.

**10.** Convert the following base five numbers to base ten:
   (a) 302, (b) 24, (c) 1234, (d) 42344.

**11.** Convert the following base ten numbers to base five:
   (a) 109, (b) 468, (c) 6790, (d) 18 965.

**12.** Which is greater $(1073)_{10}$ or $(13242)_5$?

**13.** Perform the following additions in base 5:

| (a) 314 | (b) 1340 | (c) 2304 |
|---------|----------|----------|
| + 43    | + 444    | + 4032.  |

**14.** Perform the following multiplications in base 5:

| (a) 23 | (b) 44 | (c) 123 |
|--------|--------|---------|
| $\times$ 34 | $\times$ 13 | $\times$ 30. |

**15.** Perform the following subtractions in base 5:

| (a) 43 | (b) 103 | (c) 434 |
|--------|---------|---------|
| − 14   | − 32    | − 141.  |

**16.** Perform the following divisions in base 5:
   (a) $3131 \div 43$, (b) $430 \div 10$, (c) $42 \div 24$.

**17.** Compute $XIV + XXI + XL$.

**18.** Convert XLIX to base 5. (Hint: Go via the familiar decimal system.)

**19.** Convert $XX \div V$ to base 5.

**20.** Which is greater, $XXI - V$ or $(32)_5$?

# 5/Sets (B)

## 1. Intersection of two sets

In Chapter 1 we defined a binary operation on sets. This operation was called "forming the union of two sets" and was denoted by the symbol $\cup$. If

$$A = \{2, 5, 3, 7, 4\}$$

and

$$B = \{1, 9, 4, 5, 10, 7\},$$

then the union of these two sets is given by

$$A \cup B = \{1, 2, 3, 4, 5, 7, 9, 10\}.$$

Another useful operation on sets is that of forming the **intersection** of two sets. This operation is also a binary one because it associates with each *pair* of sets a *single* set. The symbol for intersection is $\cap$ and the set $A \cap B$ with $A$ and $B$ defined as above is given by

$$A \cap B = \{4, 5, 7\}.$$

Note that the intersection of two sets $A$ and $B$ is a set consisting of those elements which are in both $A$ and $B$. In contrast, the union of two sets $A$ and $B$ is a set consisting of all those elements which are in $A$ *or* in $B$ *or* in both $A$ and $B$.

The term "intersection" is an appropriate one for the concept involved. If Third Avenue runs east-west and Fifth Street runs north-south, then the intersection of Third Avenue and Fifth Street consists of the region that the two streets have in common.

It is quite possible that two sets may not have any elements in common at all. When this is the case, we say that the intersection of the two sets is empty—meaning that it is the empty set. For example, if

$$C = \{1, 3, 5, 7, \ldots, 37\}$$

and

$$D = \{2, 4, 6, 8, \ldots, 18\},$$

then

$$C \cap D = \varnothing.$$

Sets such as $C$ and $D$ whose intersection is the empty set are said to be **disjoint**. The significance of this term will become apparent in Section 3 of this chapter.

From this extreme case we can go to the other where the intersection is one of the two sets. To illustrate this, let

$$E = \{3, 6, 9, 12, 15, 18, 21, 24\}$$

and

$$F = \{6, 12, 18, 24\}.$$

Then

$$E \cap F = \{6, 12, 18, 24\} = F.$$

Thus we have the situation that if $R$ and $S$ are any two sets whatever such that $n(R) < n(S)$, then the number of elements in the intersection of $R$ and $S$ is *at most equal to* the number of elements in $R$. In symbols,

$$n(R \cap S) \leq n(R).$$

Note that the symbol "$\leq$" is read "is at most equal to." This is more easily understood than the literal "is less than or equal to." The latter might be called a literal translation in contrast with the former free translation.

It should be clear that if $R$ and $S$ are any two sets whatever, then the number of elements in the intersection of $R$ and $S$ is *at least equal to* zero. In symbols,

$$n(R \cap S) \geq 0.$$

The symbol "$\geq$" is translated freely as "is at least equal to" and literally as "is greater than or equal to."

Putting the above ideas together into one statement results in

$$0 \leq n(R \cap S) \leq n(R).$$

This is read, "the number of elements in the intersection of sets $R$ and $S$ is at least equal to zero and at most equal to the number of elements in $R$" (provided that $n(R) < n(S)$ as before, of course).

Using the concept of intersection we can now also specify the number of elements in the union of two arbitrary sets. Let $R$ and $S$ be two such sets. Then

$$n(R \cup S) = n(R) + n(S) - n(R \cap S).$$

This follows from the way we form the union of two sets—we do not repeat elements which occur in both sets. Thus in the above formula those elements which are counted twice (that is, are found in the intersection) are subtracted.

It is appropriate to mention here that some elementary texts introduce the topic of addition of natural numbers by using the union of disjoint sets. For example, if

$$A = \{\Delta, *, 0\}$$

and

$$B = \{h, e\},$$

then

$$A \cup B = \{\Delta, *, 0, h, e\}$$

and

$$n(A \cup B) = n(A) + n(B),$$

that is,

$$5 = 3 + 2.$$

Using this method, the pupil forms the union of disjoint sets and (by counting!) determines the sum of two natural numbers.

Finally, we note that sets exhibit the property of *closure* under the binary operation $\cap$. This fact can also be expressed by saying that the universe is closed under the operation $\cap$. This means that if we take any two sets from the universe of discourse, their intersection will be a set from the same universe.

## 2. Subsets

In the preceding section we hinted at the concept we are now about to introduce. The question could very well have been asked: Under what conditions is the intersection of two sets precisely one of the sets?

Suppose that the universe of discourse is the set $N$ of natural numbers. Let

$$A = \{1, 2, 3, 4, 5, 6, 7\}$$

and

$$B = \{2, 4, 6\}.$$

This is a case where $A \cap B = B$. Why is this so? Because all the elements of $B$ are also elements of $A$. We describe this condition by saying that $B$ is a **subset** of $A$. This symbol for "is a subset of" is $\subseteq$. Hence we write $B \subseteq A$. This relation between the sets $B$ and $A$ can also be read in the reverse direction. In this case we say $A$ is a **superset** of $B$. This terminology, however, is not common.

We are ready now to state a mathematical definition and then test various sets in order to determine whether they satisfy the definition.

**Definition:** A set $B$ is said to be a subset of a set $A$ if every element of $B$ is also an element of $A$. (The key words here are the words "every" and "also.")

Now let us examine the various subsets of an arbitrary set $B$. First, is $B$ a subset of $B$? It is if $B$ satisfies the above definition. Is it true that every element of $B$ is also an element of $B$? Of course this is true! Hence every set is a subset of itself! It sounds strange but we must accept it on the basis of the definition we have given.

Next, is the empty set a subset of $B$? Is every element of $\varnothing$ also an element of $B$! Yes, because $\varnothing$ has no elements, hence $\varnothing$ is a subset of every set.

Thus every set immediately has two subsets—itself and the empty set. What other subsets does it have? Let us investigate a simple case and attempt to draw some generalizations from it. This is a powerful method in mathematics. It is known as *inductive reasoning*—going from the particular to the general.

Let the set $B$ be defined as

$$B = \{1, 4, 6\}$$

and let us list all the subsets of $B$. We have $B$, $\varnothing$, $\{1\}$, $\{4\}$, $\{6\}$,

$\{1, 4\}$, $\{1, 6\}$, $\{4, 6\}$. No other subsets are possible, hence we conclude that a set of three elements has a total of eight subsets.

A set of two elements, say

$$C = \{5, 7\}$$

has four subsets, $C$, $\varnothing$, $\{5\}$, $\{7\}$. A set consisting of a single element has two subsets, itself and the empty set.

We do not have enough information to make a generalization, so we consider a set having four elements. Let

$$D = \{3, 6, 8, 10\}.$$

By working carefully we can list all the subsets of $D$. They are $D$, $\varnothing$, $\{3\}$, $\{6\}$, $\{8\}$, $\{10\}$, $\{3, 6\}$, $\{3, 8\}$, $\{3, 10\}$, $\{6, 8\}$, $\{6, 10\}$, $\{8, 10\}$, $\{3, 6, 8\}$, $\{3, 6, 10\}$, $\{3, 8, 10\}$, $\{6, 8, 10\}$. In other words, a set of four elements has sixteen subsets.

Now we can examine the data that is available and try to make a generalization. The best way to look at the data is to put the figures in a table.

| No. of elements in set | No. of subsets |
|---|---|
| 0 | 1 |
| 1 | 2 |
| 2 | 4 |
| 3 | 8 |
| 4 | 16 |

Note that in order to have a complete table we included the empty set at the beginning. We leave it to the reader to make a conjecture about the number of subsets contained in a set having five elements.

If we were to make a generalization on the basis of this meager data, we could be accused of being "conclusion jumpers" of the most impetuous type. The correct procedure is to make a conjecture and then prove this conjecture. The methods of proof that may be used are beyond the scope of this book.

Some rather peculiar conditions arise when we consider sets having an infinite number of elements. As an example, if

$$N = \{1, 2, 3, 4, 5, \ldots, n, \ldots\}$$
$$T = \{3, 6, 9, 12, \ldots, 3n, \ldots\}$$
$$F = \{5, 10, 15, 20, \ldots, 5n, \ldots\}$$
$$S = \{6, 12, 18, 24, \ldots, 6n, \ldots\},$$

we have $T \subseteq N$, $F \subseteq N$, $S \subseteq N$, that is, $T$, $F$, and $S$ are each subsets of $N$. Yet, by making a one-to-one correspondence (or matching) between the elements of these sets, we can conclude that

$$n(T) = n(F) = n(S) = n(N).$$

In brief, the sets $T$, $F$, and $S$ are all countable. Here we have the seemingly paradoxical situation that a set has as many elements as there are in three of its subsets!

Some authors define a binary operation on sets called **set separation** and denoted by a minus sign. If $A$ and $B$ are sets, then $A - B$ is defined as the set of elements remaining in $A$ after the elements of set $B$ are removed. Another way of saying this is, "$A - B$ is the set of all elements in $A$ which are not in $B$." Note the resemblance of this last statement to the definition of a subset.

Subtraction can be illustrated by considering the set $A - B$ with $B$ a subset of $A$. For example, if

$$A = \{f, i, n, g, e, r\}$$

and

$$B = \{f, i, n, e\},$$

then

$$A - B = \{g, r\}$$

and

$$n(A - B) = n(A) - n(B),$$

that is,

$$2 = 6 - 4.$$

## 3. Venn diagrams

We have seen that the binary operation $\cup$ on sets can be interpreted as "or" and the binary operation $\cap$ as "and." The words "or" and "and" are basic connectives in logic where they are called "disjunction" and "conjunction" respectively. The English logician John Venn

(1834–1923) originated a diagram called a Venn diagram[1] which is useful in studying the relations between sets.

A Venn diagram does not give a picture of a set but it is a visual aid that helps us to see the relations between sets and operations on sets. The universal set $U$ is usually shown as a rectangle and other sets are indicated approximately as circles. For example, let $U$ be the set of natural numbers and let sets $A$ and $B$ be defined as follows:

$$A = \{3, 6, 9, 12, 15, \ldots\}$$
$$B = \{6, 12, 18, 24, \ldots\}.$$

In other words the set $A$ contains all the multiples of 3 and the set $B$ contains all the multiples of 6. The Venn diagram for this system is shown in Figure 5.1. Here we think of the various counting num-

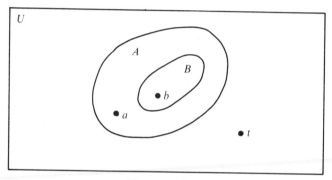

**Figure 5.1**

bers as points in the regions shown. For example, $a$ might represent 15 and $b$ might represent 18. The point $t$ might represent 2 or 10 or 13. None of these are multiples of 3 or of 6, but they *are* natural numbers. Hence they are shown within $U$ but outside of $A$ and $B$.

We also note that $B$ is completely within $A$ which means that every element of $B$ is automatically an element of $A$. But this is the same as saying that $B$ is a subset of $A$, that is, $B \subseteq A$. Since $B$ and $A$ are both subsets of $U$, we can also write

$$B \subseteq A \subseteq U.$$

This is read "$B$ is a subset of $A$ which in turn is a subset of $U$."

As another example, let

$$C = \{2, 3, 5, 7, 11, 13, 17, 19\}$$

[1] Some people refer to them as "Euler diagrams" after the Swiss mathematician Leonhard Euler (1707–1783).

Chapter 5

and
$$D = \{4, 6, 8, 9, 10, 12, 14, 15, 16, 18, 20\}.$$

The correct Venn diagram in this case is depicted in Figure 5.2. Note

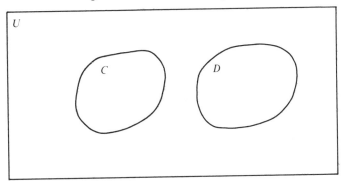

**Figure 5.2**

that this is the other extreme, namely, the two sets $C$ and $D$ have nothing in common; their intersection is empty; they are **disjoint** sets. The diagram indicates why we use the word "disjoint." In symbols,

$$C \cap D = \varnothing.$$

Between the two extremes we have an infinite number of possibilities. One of these will be illustrated next. Suppose that

$$E = \{2, 3, 5, 6, 9, 12\}$$

and

$$F = \{1, 2, 4, 5, 6, 7, 8, 9\}.$$

Then we would indicate $E$ and $F$ on a Venn diagram as in Figure 5.3.

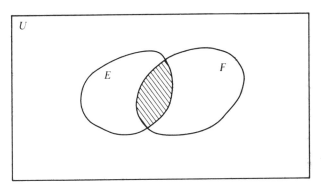

**Figure 5.3**

In the cross-hatched region we would find 2, 5, 6, and 9. To the left of the cross-hatched region, but within $E$, we would find 3 and 12. To the right of the cross hatched region, but within $F$, we would find 1, 4, 7, and 8.

If we had to consider three sets instead of two the situation would become more complicated. Suppose that each of the three sets intersects each of the other two. This can be indicated in a Venn diagram (Figure 5.4).

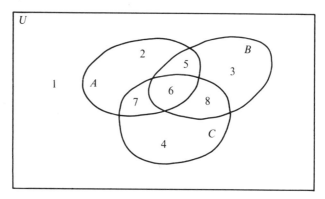

**Figure 5.4**

Notice that we have placed numbers inside of the various regions. For example, region 3 includes those elements which are in $B$ but not in $A$ or $C$; region 7 includes those elements which are common to $A$ and $C$ but which are not in $B$; region 1 includes those elements which are not in $A$ or $B$ or $C$, and so forth.

We can now illustrate the two binary operations on sets $\cup$ and $\cap$.

    1. $A \cup B$ consists of regions 2, 3, 5, 6, 7, and 8.

    2. $A \cap B$ consists of regions 5 and 6.

    3. $A \cup C$ consists of regions 2, 4, 5, 6, 7, and 8.

    4. $A \cap C$ consists of regions 6 and 7.

    5. $B \cup C$ consists of regions 3, 4, 5, 6, 7, and 8.

    6. $B \cap C$ consists of regions 6 and 8.

    7. $B \cup U$ consists of regions 1, 2, 3, 4, 5, 6, 7, and 8.

    8. $B \cap U$ consists of regions 3, 5, 6, and 8.

As a specific non-numerical example of the above ideas, let $U$ be the students at Doe College. Further, let $A$ be the set of students who are taking a humanities course, $B$ the set of students taking a science course, and $C$ the set of students involved in some extra-curricular activity. What is $(A \cap B) \cap (A \cap C)$?

An effective way of presenting Venn diagrams in the classroom is to use colored chalk for the various regions. The teacher can then talk about the region that is both red and yellow, or the region that is neither blue nor white.

## Exercises 5B

**1.** Give an example of two infinite (countable) sets whose intersection is empty.

**2.** If $B$ is the set of brown-haired girls in the class and $R$ is the set of girls in the class wearing something red, how would you describe $B \cap R$? What about $R \cap B$? What about $B \cup R$?

**3.** It can be proved (by a method called *mathematical induction*) that a set having $n$ elements has a total of $2^n$ subsets. How many subsets does the following set have?

$$C = \{1, 2, 3, \ldots, 8\}.$$

**4.** Draw a Venn diagram showing the set $C$ of exercise 3 and also the sets

$$D = \{2, 4, 6, 7, 8\}$$

and

$$E = \{4, 6\}.$$

**5.** What elements are contained in each of the following sets which were described in exercises 3 and 4?

(a) $C \cap D$              (e) $C \cup E$

(b) $D \cap E$              (f) $(D \cup E) \cap (E \cap \varnothing)$

(c) $C \cap E$              (g) $(C \cap D) \cap E$

(d) $D \cup E$              (h) $C \cap (D \cap E)$.

**6.** If two arbitrary sets $M$ and $N$ satisfy the relations $M \subseteq N$ and $N \subseteq M$, what conclusion can you draw?

**7.** Given that $n(S) = 6$ and $n(T) = 4$. Explain why $S \nsubseteq T$. Does it necessarily follow that $T \subseteq S$? Why?

**8.** Show a Venn diagram that describes the following situation:
$$U = \{1, 2, 3, \ldots, 12\}$$
$$A = \{2, 1, 5, 7\}$$
$$B = \{3, 4, 2, 5\}$$
$$D = \{4, 6, 9, 3, 7, 5\}$$
$$E = \{3, 6, 9\}.$$

**9.** Referring to exercise 8, in which intersections are each of the following elements? (Hint: For example $2 \in A \cap B$.)

(a) 5      (b) 3      (c) 6 and 9      (d) 7      (e) 11.

**10.** Referring to exercise 8, which elements are contained in each of the following:

(a) $(A \cap B) \cap (A \cap D)$

(b) $(B \cup E) \cap (A \cap D)$

(c) $(A \cap D) \cup (B \cap E)$.

**11.** List all the subsets of the set
$$A = \{2, 1, 5, 7\}.$$

**12.** How many subsets does the empty set have? Recalling (exercise 3) that the total number of subsets of a set of $n$ elements is $2^n$, what conclusions might you draw about the value of $2^0$?

**13.** In a class of brown-haired girls some have brown eyes and some have blue eyes. Illustrate this situation with a Venn diagram.

**14.** In a poll taken of 120 boys in a certain class 30 said their favorite sport was basketball, 22 preferred football and 16 preferred tennis. A number had two favorite sports—32 liked basketball and football equally well, 17 preferred football and tennis, while 27 voted for basketball and tennis. Analyze these figures for consistency by drawing a Venn diagram.

**15.** In exercise 14 how many boys liked all three sports? How many voted for basketball and tennis but not football?

**16.** If $A \subseteq B$ and $B \subseteq C$, does it follow that $A \subseteq C$? Explain.

**17.** Analyze the following statement for various definitions of $D$ and $E$. Is the statement correct?
$$D \cap E \subseteq D \cup E.$$

**18.** What two interpretations can be given to the expression,
$$A \cap B \cup C,$$

for arbitrary sets $A$, $B$, and $C$? How can the meaning of the expression be clarified?

# 6/The Real Number System (B)

## 1. Whole numbers

In Chapter 2 we discussed the set $N$ of natural (or counting) numbers. In some ways the word "counting" is a misnomer because the number one is really not at the beginning of a counting process. For example, on a ruler we do not find the number one at the left end but one inch from the end. Again, when we see a sign on the highway stating, "Speedometer check ahead," we know that the next sign will read, "0 mile."

Thus we need to augment our set $N$ to include a number less than one, namely, *zero*. We define the set

$$W = \{0, 1, 2, 3, 4, 5, \ldots\}$$

as the set of **whole numbers.**

We note that the set $W$ is denumerable even though it has one more element than the set $N$. To see this more clearly, we look at both sets simultaneously.

$$N = \{1, 2, 3, 4, 5, \ldots, n, \ldots\}$$
$$W = \{0, 1, 2, 3, 4, \ldots, n - 1, \ldots\}.$$

The proper matching process is to match every natural number $n$ with the whole number $n - 1$, that is, $n \leftrightarrow n - 1$. This one-to-one correspondence between the elements of the two sets proves that $W$ is denumerable.

We note also that every element of $N$ is also an element of $W$, hence $N$ is a subset of $W$: $N \subseteq W$. In fact, we will see that, as we develop the real number system, each set will be a subset of the next one.

## 2. Zero, the additive identity

In Chapter 2 we discussed the axioms (or properties) of the natural numbers. We list them now for reference.

**A1.** For any two natural numbers $a$ and $b$, $a + b$ is a natural number (closure under addition).

**A2.** For any two natural numbers $a$ and $b$, $a + b = b + a$ (commutative law of addition).

**A3.** For any three natural numbers $a$, $b$, and $c$, $a + (b + c) = (a + b) + c$ (associative law of addition).

**M1.** For any two natural numbers $a$ and $b$, $a \times b$ is a natural number (closure under multiplication).

**M2.** For any two natural numbers $a$ and $b$, $a \times b = b \times a$ (commutative law of multiplication).

**M3.** For any three natural numbers $a$, $b$, and $c$,

$$a \times (b \times c) = (a \times b) \times c$$

(associative law of multiplication).

**M4.** For any natural number $a$, $a \times 1 = a$
(one, the multiplicative identity).

**D.** For any three natural numbers $a$, $b$, and $c$,

$$a \times (b + c) = (a \times b) + (a \times c)$$

(distributive law of multiplication over addition).

We next inquire whether these properties also apply to the set $W$ of whole numbers. It should be clear that this question can be answered quite easily once we determine how zero behaves with respect to addition and multiplication.

Addition was defined as counting to the right so that $4 + 3$ means "start at four and count forward three." Similarly, $4 + 1$ means "start at four and count forward one." Thus it is natural to define $4 + 0$ to mean "start at four and count forward zero, that is, *don't count forward.*" Hence $4 + 0 = 4$.

In the previous paragraph there is nothing magic about the number four—we could have used any other natural number. From the above discussion we can also conclude that $0 + 0 = 0$. Now we can state an axiom for the whole numbers which did not exist for the natural numbers. We have

**A4.** For any whole number $a$, $a + 0 = a$.

We note the resemblance between this axiom and **M4.** Now we have a number unchanged when zero is added to it. We call zero **the additive identity.** This property of zero is not possessed by any other number.

Thus the numbers zero and one have special properties and for this reason occupy a special place in the hierarchy of numbers. We will see later that, while adding zero to a number does not change the number, this is a useful operation in mathematics.

Knowing that $0 + 0 = 0$ now enables us to conclude that $3 \times 0 = 0$ since $3 \times 0 = 0 + 0 + 0 = (0 + 0) + 0 = 0 + 0 = 0$. Notice how the properties of our number system are applied. Again the number 3 was used as an example and we have in general,

$$a \times 0 = 0 \text{ for any whole number } a.$$

In words, multiplying a number by zero always produces zero. Because of this property of zero we sometimes refer to zero as an *annihilator* under multiplication. We remark that the above argument does not explain why $0 \times 0 = 0$. It is nevertheless true and will be proved in Chapter 10.

The properties of the whole numbers are the same as those of the natural numbers with the single exception that property A4 has been added. Thus, in the list of **A1** to **A3, M1** to **M4,** and **D** at the beginning of this section we can replace the words "natural number" by "whole number."

## 3. Rational numbers

So far the number line has the appearance shown in Figure 6.1.

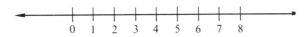

**Figure 6.1**

Note that we have extended the line to the left of zero. This was done in order to provide some hint of what is to come—the negative numbers will be located here later.

We next extend our number system so that we have not only the whole numbers but also numbers like ⅓, 3½, 7.05, and so on. This is done by introducing the concept of a rational number. A **rational number** is a number that can be written in the form $w/n$ where $n$ is some natural number and $w$ is a whole number. The set of all such numbers is called the *set of rational numbers*. Denoting this set by $R$ we can write $$R = \{w/n \mid w \in W,\, n \in N\}.$$

Although $R$ is an infinite set, we can list its elements in a systematic way in the following fashion:

$$\begin{array}{llllll}
{}^0\!/_1, & {}^1\!/_1, & {}^2\!/_1, & {}^3\!/_1, & {}^4\!/_1, & {}^5\!/_1, & \ldots \\
{}^0\!/_2, & {}^1\!/_2, & {}^2\!/_2, & {}^3\!/_2, & {}^4\!/_2, & {}^5\!/_2, & \ldots \\
{}^0\!/_3, & {}^1\!/_3, & {}^2\!/_3, & {}^3\!/_3, & {}^4\!/_3, & {}^5\!/_3, & \ldots \\
{}^0\!/_4, & {}^1\!/_4, & {}^2\!/_4, & {}^3\!/_4, & {}^4\!/_4, & {}^5\!/_4, & \ldots \\
{}^0\!/_5, & {}^1\!/_5, & {}^2\!/_5, & {}^3\!/_5, & {}^4\!/_5, & {}^5\!/_5, & \ldots
\end{array}$$

. . .

Of course there are many duplications in this listing but, nevertheless, *every* [1] rational number appears in the table. For example, ⅓ is the second number in the third row, 3½ is the eighth number in the second row (⁷⁄₂), 7.05 is the 142nd number in the 20th row (¹⁴¹⁄₂₀), and so on.

The word "rational" contains the word "ratio" and, in fact, rational numbers can be expressed as ratios. Instead of ⁷⁄₂ (seven halves) we can also say "the ratio of 7 to 2." When written as ⁷⁄₂ this rational number is said to be in *fractional form*.[2] The 7 is called the **numerator**

---

[1] Meaning every number studied so far. Negative numbers will be discussed in Chapter 10.

[2] In contrast to 3.5 which is in *decimal* form and 3½ which is in *mixed* form, for example.

and the 2 is called the **denominator.** Thus an alternate definition of a rational number is the following: A rational number can be written as a fraction whose numerator is a whole number and whose denominator is a natural number.

The fractional form also implies *division*, the inverse of multiplication. We say $\%_3 = 6 \div 3 = 2$ because $2 \times 3 = 6$. Note how the three numbers 6, 3, and 2 are written in *reverse* order when the *inverse* operation is used. Other examples are the following:

$$\%_2 = 2 \div 2 = 1 \text{ because } 1 \times 2 = 2$$
$$\%_5 = 5 \div 5 = 1 \text{ because } 1 \times 5 = 5$$
$$\%_3 = 0 \div 3 = 0 \text{ because } 0 \times 3 = 0$$
$$\%_7 = 0 \div 7 = 0 \text{ because } 0 \times 7 = 0$$

$\%_0$ is undefined because in our definition of rational number the denominator must be a natural number and zero is not a natural number.

We can make a number of observations as we look at the table of rational numbers. The set of rational numbers includes all the whole numbers. In fact the whole numbers appear in the first row of the table since $\%_1 = 0$, $\%_1 = 1$, $\%_1 = 2$, etc. In other words, the set of whole numbers (and also the set of natural numbers) is a subset of the set of rational numbers. In symbols,

$$N \subseteq W \subseteq R.$$

A Venn diagram illustrating the above situation is shown in Figure 6.2.

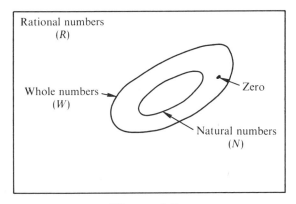

**Figure 6.2**

We note also that most of the duplications occurring in a listing of the rational numbers are due to the fact that a number has many forms. For example, the number two can be written in a great many different ways. Some of these are given in the following list:

$$2, \ 1 + 1, \ 5 - 3, \ \text{II}, \ \text{deux}, \ \text{zwei}, \ \text{kettö}, \ \tfrac{2}{1}, \ \tfrac{4}{2}, \ \tfrac{6}{3}, \ \tfrac{10}{5}.$$

The last four forms are of particular interest to us now. Beginning with $\tfrac{2}{1}$ we can obtain the other forms by multiplying $\tfrac{2}{1}$ by one, the multiplicative identity. Thus $\tfrac{2}{1} \times \tfrac{2}{2} = \tfrac{4}{2}$, $\tfrac{2}{1} \times \tfrac{3}{3} = \tfrac{6}{3}$, $\tfrac{2}{1} \times \tfrac{5}{5} = \tfrac{10}{5}$, etc. We are using here not only different forms of the multiplicative identity but also the well-known definition of multiplication of rational numbers, namely,

$$a/b \times c/d = (a \times c)/(b \times d).$$

Because $a/1 = a$ for any whole number $a$, we conclude that 1 is the identity in division as well as in multiplication. In other words, $a \div 1 = a$ for any whole number $a$. For multiplication we had $a \times 1 = 1 \times a = a$ for any whole number $a$. The inverse of $a \times 1 = a$ is $a \div 1 = a$ and this holds for any whole number $a$. The inverse of $1 \times a = a$ is $a \div a = 1$ and this holds for any natural number $a$.

If we take the listing of the rational numbers and a number line, we can locate each rational number (omitting duplications) on a number line. Figure 6.3 shows what we would have after locating the first six numbers in the second and third lines of the listing.

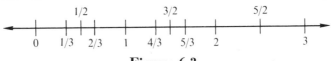

**Figure 6.3**

It can be seen that if we were to continue this process, we could completely cover the number line *for all practical* purposes. [3] It is a fact that between any two rational numbers—no matter how close together they are—there is another rational number. Take, for example, the two numbers $\tfrac{101}{103}$ and $\tfrac{102}{103}$. Both of these numbers are very near to 1 and it would require quite a large scale on a number line to distinguish between them. Yet

$$\tfrac{101}{103} = \tfrac{101}{103} \times 1 = \tfrac{101}{103} \times \tfrac{2}{2} = \tfrac{202}{206}$$

and

$$\tfrac{102}{103} = \tfrac{102}{103} \times 1 = \tfrac{102}{103} \times \tfrac{2}{2} = \tfrac{204}{206},$$

[3] We will see the full import of this phrase in Chapter 10.

so that $\frac{203}{206}$ is a rational number between $\frac{101}{103}$ and $\frac{102}{103}$. In symbols,

$$\frac{101}{103} < \frac{203}{206} < \frac{102}{103}.$$

In a similar manner we could find a rational number between $\frac{101}{103}$ and $\frac{203}{206}$. This process could be continued indefinitely so that we might conclude that the rational numbers *completely* cover the number line. That this is far from the truth is one of the most interesting facts about the real number system. A more complete discussion of these ideas will be given in Chapter 10.

We conclude this section with the remark that the set $R$ is denumerable, that is, its elements can be put into one-to-one correspondence with the elements of the set $N$.

## 4. Reciprocals

All of the properties of the whole numbers hold also for the rational numbers. [4] We list these for reference. Recall that the set $R$ is the set of rational numbers.

**A1.** If $a$ and $b$ are any two elements of $R$, then $a + b$ is an element of $R$.

**A2.** If $a$ and $b$ are any two elements of $R$, then $a + b = b + a$.

**A3.** If $a$, $b$, and $c$ are any three elements of $R$, then $a + (b + c) = (a + b) + c$.

**A4.** If $a$ is any element of $R$, then $a + 0 = a$.

**M1.** If $a$ and $b$ are any two elements of $R$, then $a \times b$ is an element of $R$.

**M2.** If $a$ and $b$ are any two elements of $R$, then $a \times b = b \times a$.

**M3.** If $a$, $b$, and $c$ are any three elements of $R$, then $a \times (b \times c) = (a \times b) \times c$.

**M4.** If $a$ is any element of $R$, then $a \times 1 = a$.

**D.** If $a$, $b$, and $c$ are any three elements of $R$, then $a \times (b + c) = (a \times b) + (a \times c)$.

[4] These properties can be *proved* for the rational numbers using the usual definitions of addition, multiplication and equality of rational numbers.

You should certainly suspect by now that the set $R$ must possess more than the nine properties listed above. After all, the set $W$, a subset of $R$, has all these properties, so why shouldn't $R$ have even more? As a matter of fact, the set $R$ does have a property that $W$ does not have. In order to describe this property we need to understand the term "reciprocal."

A rational number is said to be the **reciprocal** of another rational number if the product of the two numbers is one. Thus $\frac{2}{3}$ is the reciprocal of $\frac{3}{2}$ because $\frac{2}{3} \times \frac{3}{2} = 1$. Similarly, 2 is the reciprocal of $\frac{1}{2}$, $\frac{11}{7}$ of $\frac{7}{11}$, $\frac{1}{3}$ of 3, $\frac{3}{10}$ of $\frac{10}{3}$. Every rational number except zero has a reciprocal since there is *no* rational number which when multiplied by zero will yield *one*. (Recall that $a \times 0 = 0$ for any rational number $a$.)

Introducing reciprocals may seem like adding unnecessary complications to our number system but reciprocals allow us to *divide* rational numbers. Suppose we seek the answer to $\frac{2}{3} \div \frac{3}{5}$. One of the mysterious rules of the "old" mathematics was "invert the divisor and multiply." Why this produced the correct result was often neither understood nor questioned.

Today we attack the problem $\frac{2}{3} \div \frac{3}{5}$ in the following manner. We write $\frac{2}{3} \div \frac{3}{5} = x$ and wish to find the value of $x$. We know that multiplication and division are inverse processes, hence $\frac{2}{3} \div \frac{3}{5} = x$ can also be written as $x \times \frac{3}{5} = \frac{2}{3}$. Thus the question is, "what number multiplied by $\frac{3}{5}$ will yield $\frac{2}{3}$?"

We don't let the letter $x$ scare us to death, thinking that we're "doing algebra," but rather we borrow a trick from the first and second grades. We restate the problem as follows: $\square \times \frac{3}{5} = \frac{2}{3}$ and ask what number should be put into the box.

Now the reasoning goes something like this. If we are to multiply some number by $\frac{3}{5}$ and obtain $\frac{2}{3}$, obviously we must somehow "get rid of the $\frac{3}{5}$." One way to do this is to multiply $\frac{3}{5}$ by its reciprocal, $\frac{5}{3}$. But this will produce 1, not the desired $\frac{2}{3}$. Hence the number in the box must be $\frac{2}{3} \times \frac{5}{3}$. In other words,

$$\boxed{\frac{2}{3} \times \frac{5}{3}} \times \frac{3}{5} = \frac{2}{3}.$$

This, however, is equivalent to saying that

$$\frac{2}{3} \div \frac{3}{5} = \frac{2}{3} \times \frac{5}{3}.$$

We can now say with assurance that $2/3 \div 3/5 = 2/3 \times 5/3 = {}^{10}/_9$, using the definition of multiplication of rational numbers. Reciprocals thus provide a way to perform the inverse of multiplication of rational numbers. Since every rational number (except zero) has a reciprocal and, since these reciprocals are also rational numbers, we can state

**M5.** For every rational number $a$ (except zero) there is a reciprocal, call it $a^{-1}$, such that $a \times a^{-1} = 1$.

For example, the reciprocal of $2/1$ is $1/2$ because $2/1 \times 1/2 = 1$. We can also say, of course, that $1 \div 1/2 = 2/1$. Because of the commutative property of multiplication of rational numbers it is also true that $1/2 \times 2/1 = 1$, hence $1 \div 2/1 = 1/2$.

Another way of arriving at the previous result is to reason as follows. Suppose we have two rational numbers, say $4/7$ and $2/9$, and we want to find the answer to $4/7 \div 2/9$. We can write

$$4/7 \div 2/9 = \frac{4/7}{2/9}.$$

Then we can multiply this rational number by one in the form $\dfrac{9/2}{9/2}$.

Now we have

$$\frac{4/7}{2/9} \times \frac{9/2}{9/2} = \frac{(4/7 \times 9/2)}{(2/9 \times 9/2)}$$
$$= \frac{{}^{36}/_{14}}{1}$$
$$= {}^{36}/_{14}$$
$$= {}^{18}/_7.$$

Note that $9/2$ was chosen because it is the reciprocal of the $2/9$ in the denominator.

The reciprocal of a rational number is also called the "multiplicative inverse." A natural question at this point is to ask if there is such a thing as an "additive inverse." The answer to this will have to be postponed to Chapter 10.

## 5. Square root by an ancient method

We have already discussed *binary* operations. Some of these, like $+$,

$\times$, $-$, $\div$, were operations on pairs of numbers that produced a single number. Others, like $\cup$ and $\cap$, were used with sets.

Now we discuss a *unary* operation, one that will produce a number when applied to a single number. Such a unary operation [5] is that of finding the *square root* of a number. The symbol for this operation is $\sqrt{\phantom{x}}$, and the number whose square root is sought is placed within the symbol. Thus $\sqrt{36}$ means: the number whose square is 36, that is, the number which when multiplied by itself yields 36. Clearly, 6 qualifies in this example because $6^2 = 6 \times 6 = 36$. Hence we write

$$\sqrt{36} = 6$$
$$\sqrt{49} = 7$$
$$\sqrt{225} = 15$$
$$\sqrt{9} = 3$$
$$\sqrt{1} = 1$$
$$\sqrt{0} = 0.$$

This is all well and good but what do we do about $\sqrt{40}$ or $\sqrt{252}$ or $\sqrt{1369}$? There is an algorithm, or computing scheme, that was used in the "old" mathematics to find the square root of a number. The process consisted of grouping the numerals by twos starting at the decimal point, doubling the answer at each step, and so on. It was a method difficult to teach, difficult to learn, and often forgotten in a short time.

Today in the "new" mathematics we teach an algorithm which can be called the *Heroian algorithm* since it is credited to Hero (born about 100 B.C.) of Alexandria. We illustrate with an example.

Suppose we wish to find the square root of 743. This means that we seek a number which when multiplied by itself will be 743 or come as close to 743 as we wish. We begin by guessing a number. It is not a wild guess, however, because we know that

$$10 \times 10 = 100$$

and

$$30 \times 30 = 900.$$

Thus we guess some number between 10 and 30 but closer to 30, say

[5] Another unary operation will be introduced in Chapter 9.

27. If 27 is a correct guess, then dividing 743 by 27 should yield 27. However,[6]

$$743 \div 27 \doteq 27.5.$$

This means that 27.5 does not qualify as $\sqrt{743}$ because it is too large and 27 does not qualify because it is too small. The Heroian algorithm quite naturally considers the *average* of the two numbers, that is, $\dfrac{27 + 27.5}{2} = 27.25$ as a better approximation to $\sqrt{743}$. But

$$743 \div 27.25 \doteq 27.266,$$

which shows that 27.25 is too small, while 27.266 is too large. The average of these, $\dfrac{27.25 + 27.266}{2} = 27.258$ can now be taken as a final approximation or it can be rounded to 27.26 or carried out to more decimals by further applications of the method.

This method has a number of advantages: it uses ordinary arithmetic processes; the process can be stopped at any point; any desired degree of accuracy may be obtained; it is self-correcting, meaning that the result can be obtained in spite of occasional arithmetic errors; it does not require an accurate initial guess; and it gives the user a good understanding of square root.

When it comes to finding $\sqrt{1369}$ we begin with 35 since $30 \times 30 = 900$ and $40 \times 40 = 1600$. Then the work proceeds as follows:

$$1369 \div 35 \doteq 39$$
$$\frac{39 + 35}{2} = 37$$
$$1369 \div 37 = 37.$$

Hence $\sqrt{1369} = 37$, that is, 1369 is a *perfect square*.

In this section we have examined a unary operation—finding the square root of a number. This is a fairly complex operation consisting of making an educated first guess, performing successive divisions and averagings, and using proper judgment to determine when the process should terminate. We know that in some cases the process terminates (e.g. in finding the square root of 1369 or of 72.25). We suspect that

[6] The symbol " $\doteq$ " is read "is *approximately* equal to."

in some cases the process never ends, making the square root of a number an elusive thing, impossible to pin down. We may find numbers which are a little smaller and others which are a little larger than the required number and, perhaps this is the best we can do. In Chapter 10 we will pursue this matter.

## Exercises 6B

1. What distinguishing characteristic does the distributive property have which is not shared by the other properties of the whole numbers?

2. Prove that the set $W$ of whole numbers is not closed under subtraction.

3. Prove that the set $W$ of whole numbers is not closed under division.

4. Write the number six in eight different ways.

5. Give the location of $2\frac{2}{7}$ in the listing of the rational numbers.

6. Prove that 3.1416 is a rational number.

7. Find a rational number between $10\frac{1}{103}$ and $20\frac{3}{206}$.

8. Prove that the set $R$ of rational numbers is not closed under subtraction.

9. Find the reciprocals of each of the following:

$$10, \ 2\frac{2}{7}, \ 5\frac{1}{3}, \ 8.2, \ 19.$$

10. What is $\sqrt{40}$ to two decimal places?

11. Make (and justify) a first guess of the value of $\sqrt{252}$. Then compute the square root to two decimal places.

12. Multiply the answer to exercise 11 by itself and compare the product with 252.

13. Start with 10 as a first guess and compute $\sqrt{40}$ to two decimal places. Compare the work with that done in exercise 10.

14. Find $\sqrt{72.25}$.

15. Is it true that $\sqrt{9} + \sqrt{4} = \sqrt{13}$? Explain.

16. Is it true that $\sqrt{9} \times \sqrt{4} = \sqrt{36}$? Explain.

# 7/*Geometry* (B)

## 1. What is an angle?

In geometry, more than in any other branch of mathematics, set notation and language have clarified matters. One can get an appreciation of this clarification by comparing the modern definition of an angle with those given by graduates of the "old school."

Drawing upon the idea in Chapter 3, namely, that a ray is a set of points and that one of these points is an end-point, we formulate the following definition. An **angle** is the union of two rays which have a common end-point but which do not lie on the same line.[1] A pictorial representation of an angle is given in Figure 7.1.

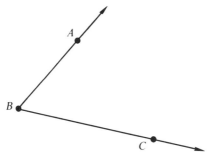

**Figure 7.1**

Here the two rays are $\overrightarrow{BA}$ and $\overrightarrow{BC}$ and their common end-point is the point $B$. The two rays do *not* lie on the same line, hence the definition given is satisfied by the angle shown in the figure. The common end-point $B$ is called the **vertex** of the angle. The angle itself is desig-

[1] This last restriction will be removed later.

nated as $\angle ABC$ or as $\angle CBA$, the essential point being that the vertex is by convention the middle one of the three letters. The symbol "$\angle$" is read "angle."

Since an angle is a union of two sets of points, it is itself a set of points. In other words, when we say, "the angle ABC" we are talking about a set of points—the points lying on the two rays. Compare this concept with those mistakenly held by many; that an angle is "the amount of turning of a line" or "the area included between two lines," and others.

To measure angles we need a unit of measure which is itself an angle. The most common standard unit of measure is called one degree and is obtained as follows. With a compass we first draw any circle. *Maintaining the setting* of the compass we next divide the circle into six parts by marking off distances around the circle. We then connect each of these six marks with the center by straight lines. Now the construction looks as follows (Figure 7.2).

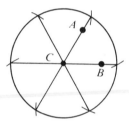

**Figure 7.2**

Looking at this figure we see six equal angles all having a common vertex $C$, the center of the circle. Continuing a custom followed for centuries and originated by the ancient Babylonians, we assign the number 60 as the measure of each of the six equal angles. This may not make sense until we recall that the Babylonians used a number system based on 60 rather than one like ours based on 10.

We see that the total measure of all six angles is 360. We still have not, however, described a unit angle—an angle whose measure is one. This is an angle obtained by subdividing one of the six equal arcs of the figure into 60 equal smaller arcs. The name given to the unit of angle measure is the **degree.** Hence the measure of $\angle ACB$ is 60 but the size of $\angle ACB$ is 60° (read 60 degrees).

Just as a ruler is convenient for measuring lengths, a *protractor* is convenient for measuring angles. Pupils should be encouraged to use a protractor early to measure and to construct various angles.

Two angles occur so often in geometry that they are given special names. An angle of 90° is called a **right** angle and an angle of 180° is called a **straight** angle.

We remark that the angle of 180° exists only if we remove a restriction in the definition of an angle. We stated that the two rays must not lie on the same straight line. If they do, as is the case with the rays $\overrightarrow{BA}$ and $\overrightarrow{BC}$ in Figure 7.3, then $\angle ABC$ is a straight angle.

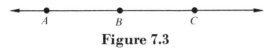

**Figure 7.3**

If the two rays lie on the same side of the common end-point, so that the two rays are $\overrightarrow{ED}$ and $\overrightarrow{EF}$, then we call $\angle DEF$ a **zero** angle. The size of such an angle is 0°.

With the above understanding of zero and straight angles we can define an angle as the union of two rays having a common end-point.

The two rays which determine an angle (other than a zero angle or a straight angle) also determine a *plane*. Hence an angle actually lies in a plane. In fact, an angle separates the plane into three parts which have nothing in common but whose union is the whole plane. We say that an angle separates the plane in which it lies into three mutually exclusive and collectively exhaustive parts.

We illustrate with Figure 7.4. Here we have $\angle ABC$ lying in the

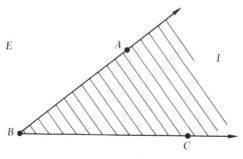

**Figure 7.4**

plane of this page. The cross-hatched region $I$ of the plane is called the **interior** of the angle—it does not include the angle. The plane region marked $E$ is the **exterior** of the angle—it does not include the angle either. Thus we have the three sets $E$, $I$, and $\angle ABC$ which are **pairwise disjoint,** meaning that the intersection of any two of them is the empty set. On the other hand, the union of $E$, $I$, and $\angle ABC$ is the entire plane.

## 2. Some plane figures

One of the simplest figures we can draw is a circle. A **circle** is a set of points all of which are at a fixed distance from a given point. The given point is called the **center** of the circle and the fixed distance is called the **radius.** Examine Figure 7.5. Here the point $C$ is the center

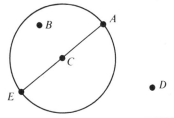

**Figure 7.5**

of the circle and the line segment $\overline{AC}$ is a radius. The points $A$ and $E$ are said to be *on* the circle, points $B$ and $C$ are in the interior of the circle, and point $D$ is exterior to the circle. Note that *of the points shown* only $A$ and $E$ are *on* the circle.

The line segment $\overline{EA}$ is called a **diameter** of the circle. If we start at $A$ and move so as always to stay on the circle, we will eventually return to $A$. The total distance we have travelled is called the **circumference** of the circle.

A circle is an example of a *simple closed curve*. The words "closed" and "curve" have the ordinary meanings but the word "simple" needs to be explained. A **simple closed curve** divides the plane into three mutually exclusive parts; those points which are *on* the curve, those points which are *interior* to the curve, and those which are *exterior* to the curve. It should be clear from this and from the previous discussion that a circle qualifies as a simple closed curve.

To further clarify this idea, consider the closed curves shown in Figure 7.6:

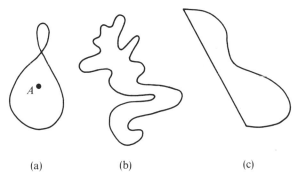

<table>
<tr><td>(a)</td><td>(b)</td><td>(c)</td></tr>
</table>

**Figure 7.6**

Of these, (a) is the only one which is not simple. The reason for this is that the point $A$ is exterior to one portion and in the interior of another. Although (b) appears to be complicated, it is simple. Attention is called to (c) where part of the "curve" is a line segment. In geometry a straight line is a special case of a curve.

We are now ready to describe a polygon. A **polygon** is a simple closed curve which is the union of line segments. In Figure 7.7 are some polygons:

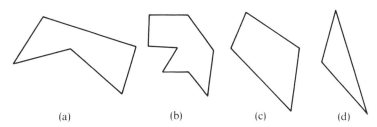

<table>
<tr><td>(a)</td><td>(b)</td><td>(c)</td><td>(d)</td></tr>
</table>

**Figure 7.7**

Polygons are classified according to the *number* of line segments of which they are formed. Thus, (a) is a *pentagon* (5 segments), (b) is an *octagon* (8 segments), (c) is a *quadrilateral* (4 segments), and (d) is a *triangle* (3 segments). Note that a polygon cannot have less than 3 segments and for this reason the triangle is a basic simple closed curve.

Consider the triangle shown in Figure 7.8:

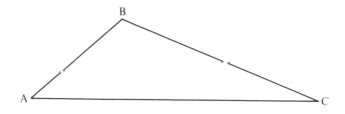

**Figure 7.8**

We refer to this as $\triangle ABC$. The points $A$, $B$, and $C$ are the three **vertices** of the triangle. Each of these vertices is the vertex of an *angle*. The three angles of this triangle are $\angle BAC$, $\angle ACB$, and $\angle CBA$. The three **sides** of this triangle are the line segments $\overline{AB}$, $\overline{BC}$, and $\overline{AC}$.

It is a property of all triangles that *the sum of their three angles is 180°*. This fact can be "discovered" by pupils quite easily. Let each student draw a triangle using a straightedge. Let the three vertices be labelled $A$, $B$, and $C$. Ask the students to determine each of the angles as accurately as possible using their protractors. Have them repeat this experiment several times using different triangles. Do not say anything about the sum but wait until someone discovers the fact. If no one does, have them measure *two* of the angles with the protractor and ask if they can determine the third angle by *some other method*. You may need to lead or nudge before a discovery is made!

If one of the angles of a triangle is 90° (a right angle), then the triangle is called a **right triangle.** It was Pythagoras (or one of his pupils)[2] who discovered the famous relation between the sides of a right triangle known as the *Pythagorean Theorem*. If the lengths of the three sides of a right triangle are $a$, $b$, and $c$, then

$$a^2 + b^2 = c^2,$$

where $c$ is the side opposite the right angle. This side is also called the **hypotenuse.** Can you prove from what has been said that it is not possible for a right triangle to have all three sides of the same length?

A triangle is called **isosceles** if two of its sides have the same length and **equilateral** if all three sides have the same length.

Quadrilaterals are also given special names according to certain characteristics. We can best list them.

[2] It was the custom in the days of Pythagoras that all discoveries by students and teachers were credited to the head of the school. Pythagoras was the "principal" of his school.

| Name | Characteristic |
|------|----------------|
| Rectangle | four right angles |
| Square | four right angles *and* four sides of equal length |
| Parallelogram | two pairs of parallel sides |
| Trapezoid | one pair of parallel sides |
| Rhombus | two pairs of parallel sides all of which have equal length. |

Notice that there is some overlapping in the above table. For example, a square is also a rectangle, a parallelogram, and a rhombus; a rhombus is also a parallelogram. We also speak of an isosceles trapezoid—one whose non-parallel sides are equal in length.

When the sides of a polygon are all equal in length and all the angles have equal measure, the adjective "regular" is prefixed to the name. The ancient Greeks made a thorough study of polygons and have left us a heritage of terms such as pentagon and hexagon.

## 3. Area of a plane region

Recall that in Chapter 3 we considered both the measure and length of line segments. We now extend these ideas to two dimensions, that is, to the plane.

In the plane we measure plane regions and the unit of measure is, of course, also a plane region. Figure 7.9 shows a plane region at the left and a unit of measure at the right.

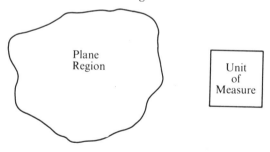

**Figure 7.9**

By the measure of the plane region we mean a *number*—how many units of measure are needed to exactly cover the region. We may think of the units of measure as square pieces of paper and use these to cover the region. We are allowed to cut a unit of measure into any number of odd-shaped pieces and use these to match the irregular boundary of the region. Suppose that to cover the region we need $4\frac{1}{4}$ of the units of measure. Then the measure of the plane region is said to be $4\frac{1}{4}$.

Just as in the case of finding lengths of line segments, there are certain units of measure in the plane that have been adopted as standard. One of these is a square whose four equal sides are each one inch in length. Such a unit of measure is called *one square inch*. If we used such a unit for the plane region of the example, we would say that the **area** of the region is $4\frac{1}{4}$ square inches.

Other useful units of measure are squares having sides of length one foot (*one square foot*), one mile (*one square mile*), one centimeter (*one square centimeter*), one meter (*one square meter*), and so on. So many different units must be considered partly because both English and metric systems are in use. There is also a practical consideration, however. It would not be convenient to use the unit called one square inch to find the area of a city, for example.

## 4. Volume

In three dimensions we find the volumes of various objects.

As a simple illustration consider the shoe box shown at the left and a unit of measure at the right (Figure 7.10).

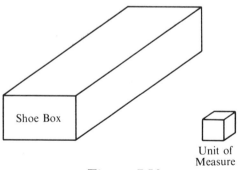

Unit of
Measure

**Figure 7.10**

Note again that the unit of measure is three dimensional like the object whose measure we seek. The unit of measure is usually a cube, that is, an object whose twelve[3] edges (line segments) all have the same length and whose six faces are squares.

We now proceed as before. To find the measure of the shoe box we must determine how many units of measure will exactly fill it. Again it is permissible to cut some units of measure apart and to use the pieces to fill the space in the shoe box.

Suppose that we find that it takes exactly 420 units of measure to fill the shoe box. (Our picture is obviously not to scale.) We say then that the *measure* of the shoe box is 420. If we are using one of the standard units of measure—a cube having each edge one inch long— then we could say that the *volume* of the shoe box is 420 *cubic inches*.

Other standard units of measure are cubes having edges of one foot (*one cubic foot*), one yard (*one cubic yard*), one mile (*one cubic mile*), one centimeter (*one cubic centimeter*), one meter (*one cubic meter*), and so on. There must be a variety of units to fit the great variety of volumes that need to be measured.

In teaching measure we have a wonderful opportunity for providing laboratory work in mathematics. Only the simplest materials are needed—rulers, graph paper, scissors, wooden blocks, hollow blocks, and various containers. The hollow blocks may be filled with water and used to measure the volumes of oddly shaped containers. The laboratory work combined with a more careful mathematical approach will lead to a deeper understanding of the subject of measure.

## 5. Discovering mensuration formulas

In two-dimensional geometry we measure area. Our unit of measure, for example, may be one square inch, that is,

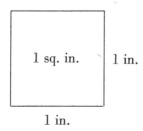

1 in.

---

[3] Only nine are shown on the figure, the other three being hidden.

Using this unit of measure we find that the measure of the area shown in the following figure is 2½. We arrive at this number because exactly two and one half of our units of measure are required to

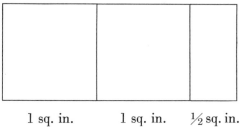

1 sq. in.          1 sq. in.          ½ sq. in.

completely cover the rectangle shown. The *measure* of the rectangle is 2½, the *unit of measure* is a square inch, the *area* is 2½ square inches. In finding the measure it is permissible (and usually necessary) to cut the unit of measure into as many parts and as many shapes as required in order to cover the region whose area we seek.

With the above technique it is not only possible to find the areas of quite unusual figures but it is possible for the pupils to *discover* formulas for the areas of various figures. Thus we have another opportunity to cater to individual differences. Discovering that the measure of the area of a rectangle can be found by multiplying the measure of its length by the measure of its width makes for exciting learning. Compare this with the former method when the teacher told the pupils that "areas is length times width." There is no comparison between the understanding gained in the two cases.

We next consider a right triangle such as $\triangle ABC$ (Figure 7.11). We

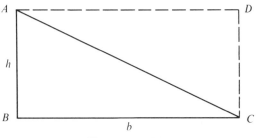

**Figure 7.11**

teach the class how to construct a line segment $\overline{CD}$ which is perpendicular to $\overline{BC}$. Then we show how to make sure that $m(\overline{CD}) = m(\overline{BA})$.[4] Finally we draw the segment $AD$. Now $ADCB$ is a rectangle and the measure of its area is given by

$$A = b \times h.$$

From this we conclude that the measure of the area of $\triangle ABC$ is

$$\tfrac{1}{2} b \times h.$$

From the right triangle we can generalize to a triangle such as $\triangle RST$ (Figure 7.12).

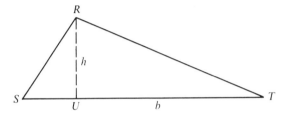

**Figure 7.12**

Now we construct $RU$ perpendicular to $ST$. Then we have

$$\text{measure of area } \triangle SRU = \tfrac{1}{2} m(RU) \times m(SU)$$
$$\text{measure of area } \triangle UTR = \tfrac{1}{2} m(RU) \times m(UT).$$

But

measure of area $\triangle STR$ = measure of area $\triangle SRU$ + measure of area $\triangle UTR$, so that by adding we obtain
measure of area $\triangle STR = \tfrac{1}{2} m(RU) \times [m(SU) + m(UT)]$

$$= \tfrac{1}{2} m(RU) \times m(ST),$$

using the distributive law. In other words, the measure of the area is again

$$\tfrac{1}{2} b \times h.$$

Next, we consider a trapezoid such as $ABCD$ (Figure 7.13). This

[4] The notation $m \ (\overline{CD})$ means "the measure of the line segment $\overline{CD}$." Recall that $m \ (\overline{CD})$ is a *number*. From this point on we will write $CD$ for $\overline{CD}$.

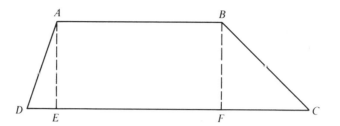

**Figure 7.13**

time we construct $AE$ and $BF$ perpendicular to $DC$. The area of $ABCD$ is the sum of the areas: $\triangle DEA + \square ABFE + \triangle FCB$. From this the students can discover that the area of a trapezoid is given by

$$h \times \left(\frac{b + b'}{2}\right)$$

where $h$ is the length of the altitude and $b$ and $b'$ are the lengths of the parallel bases.

In this section we have given some examples of teaching geometry by the "discovery" method. Discovering rules, formulas and short cuts makes the study of mathematics more exciting from both the teacher's and student's viewpoint. Moreover, discovery leads to better retention on the part of the student. Finally, if he does forget, he has a chance to *rediscover* the fact or method.

## Exercises 7B

**1.** Estimate the size of each of the following angles in degrees.

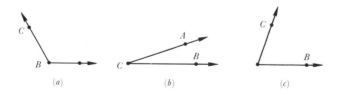

**2.** Name each of the angles in exercise 1.

**3.** Why might a 60° angle also be called 300°?

4. If one angle of a right triangle is 20°, what are the others?

5. Name the sizes of the angles in an isosceles right triangle.

6. If one of the unequal angles of an isosceles triangle is 50°, what are the other two?

7. Draw a regular hexagon. (Hint: a circle would be useful here).

8. Can 3, 4, and 5 be the measures of the sides of a right triangle? What about 5, 6, and 8? What about 5, 12, and 13?

9. Is the following statement true? All squares are rectangles but not all rectangles are squares. Explain.

10. Explain how you could deduce the relation between square inches and square feet.

11. Explain how you could deduce the relation between cubic inches and cubic feet.

12. Devise an experiment whereby the number of cubic inches in a quart can be found.

13. How many vertices does a cube have? How many right angles?

14. A polygon has angles of 60°, 60°, 120°, and 120°. Depending on how these angles are arranged, two figures can be drawn. Draw the figures and name them.

# 8/Number Theory (B)

## 1. Divisibility

In Chapter 4 we factored various numbers into their prime factors. We said, for example, that 2 and 3 were *factors* of 6. Another way of saying this is to say that 6 is *divisible* by 2 and 3.

If we are talking about rational numbers then 6, of course, is also divisible by 4 and 5. The subject of number theory, however, deals with the set $W$ of whole numbers. Hence when we say $a$ is divisible by $b$, we mean that the division leaves a zero remainder.

An equivalent way of describing a prime number is as follows: any number greater than 1 which is divisible only by 1 and itself is said to be prime.

We call attention to the fact that multiplication and division are inverse processes. In some of the work of this chapter it will be convenient to look at a problem from the viewpoint of multiplication and at other times from the viewpoint of division. For example, in

$$3 \times 8 = 24$$

we can consider that 8 is a factor of 24. On the other hand, 24 must also be divisible by 8 since 24 is the same as $3 \times 8$ and the latter is clearly divisible by 8.

In general (recall that we are using numbers from the set $W$) if

$$a \times b = c,$$

then $c$ is divisible by $a$ and $c$ is also divisible by $b$. This statement holds for all those cases in which neither $a$ nor $b$ is zero.

## 2. Greatest common divisor and the Euclidean algorithm

Factoring a number into its prime factors is useful in a number of ways and we will now investigate some of these. Suppose we wish to express the fraction 36/54 in lowest terms. We have

$$\frac{36}{54} = \frac{2^2 \times 3^2}{2 \times 3^3} = \frac{2}{3},$$

upon dividing numerator and denominator by $2 \times 3^2$ or 18.

Another way of looking at this problem is to use the concept of **greatest common divisor** (abbreviated GCD). If we list the divisors of 36 and 54, we would have

| Divisors of 36 | Divisors of 54 |
|:---:|:---:|
| 1 | 1 |
| 2 | 2 |
| 3 | 3 |
| 4 | 6 |
| 6 | 9 |
| 9 | 18 |
| 12 | 27 |
| 18 | 54 |
| 36 | |

Now the numbers 1, 2, 3, 6, 9, and 18 are called **common divisors** of 36 and 54—they divide *both* 36 and 54. Of these common divisors 18 is the greatest hence 18 is the GCD of 36 and 54.

Knowing this, we can reduce 36/54 to lowest terms as follows:

$$\frac{36}{54} = \frac{36}{54} \div 1 = \frac{36}{54} \div \frac{18}{18} = \frac{36 \div 18}{54 \div 18} = \frac{2}{3}.$$

We are assured that ⅔ is in lowest terms (if we didn't already know this) because 18 is the *largest* number that divides *both* 36 and 54.

As another example suppose we wish to find the GCD of 45 and 72. Again listing all the divisors of the two numbers, we have

| Divisors of 45 | Divisors of 72 |
|:---:|:---:|
| 1 | 1 |
| 3 | 2 |
| 5 | 3 |
| 9 | 4 |
| 15 | 6 |
| 45 | 8 |
| | 9 |
| | 12 |
| | 18 |
| | 24 |
| | 36 |
| | 72 |

From the above table we see that 1, 3, and 9 are the only numbers appearing in *both* columns. Hence 9 is the GCD of 45 and 72. We remark that this result can be easily obtained by anyone having familiarity with the multiplication tables.

It can be seen that finding all the divisors of a number is not the easiest job in the world. We had to think a bit in order to list all the divisors of 72, for example. For larger numbers, such as 4148, the job is forbidding from a practical viewpoint.

Fortunately, however, we have a method or algorithm which simplifies matters. This is known as the *Euclidean[1] algorithm*. We illustrate it by finding the GCD of 45 and 72 by this method.

We begin by dividing 72 by 45 to obtain 1 and a remainder of 27. This is equivalent to saying
$$72 = (1 \times 45) + 27.$$

Next we divide 45 by 27 to obtain 1 and a remainder of 18 or
$$45 = (1 \times 27) + 18.$$

Next we divide 27 by 18 to obtain 1 and a remainder of 9 or
$$27 = (1 \times 18) + 9.$$

Finally, we divide 18 by 9 to obtain 2 and a remainder of zero. The *last nonzero remainder* is then the GCD of the two original numbers.

[1] Named after Euclid who was born in the fourth century B.C. His work in geometry is well-known and still dominates that subject to some extent. Not so well known is the fact that he also did some pioneering work in algebra.

In this case the GCD is 9. We list the successive steps for finding the GCD of 45 and 72 for convenience as follows:

$$72 = (1 \times 45) + 27$$
$$45 = (1 \times 27) + 18$$
$$27 = (1 \times 18) + 9 \leftarrow \text{GCD of 45 and 72}$$
$$18 = (2 \times 9) + 0.$$

To analyze the situation, we can see from the first step that any integer which divides 72 and 45 must also divide 27. Why? Stated in another way, every common divisor of 45 and 27 is a divisor of 72. Why? Therefore the common divisors of 72 and 45 are the same as the common divisors of 45 and 27. Why? Thus the GCD of 72 and 45 is identical to the GCD of 45 and 27. Why? The analysis that we have made about the first line of the algorithm applies equally to the second, the third, and so forth. Hence 9 is the GCD of 18 and 27; of 27 and 45; of 45 and 72. All of this must be clearly understood so that the student who asks, "Why?" can be answered in a clear, logical manner. We must not say "Well, that is the way Euclid figured it out" or "That is what the book says."

We illustrate the Euclidean algorithm with another example. Suppose we wish to find the GCD of 180 and 252. We would proceed as follows:

$$252 = (1 \times 180) + 72$$
$$180 = (2 \times 72) + 36$$
$$72 = (2 \times 36) + 0.$$

Hence the GCD of 180 and 252 is 36. In fact, $180 = 5 \times 36$ and $252 = 7 \times 36$.

As another example consider the GCD of 7655 and 1001. The Euclidean algorithm gives

$$7655 = (7 \times 1001) + 648$$
$$1001 = (1 \times 648) + 353$$
$$648 = (1 \times 353) + 295$$
$$353 = (1 \times 295) + 58$$
$$295 = (5 \times 58) + 5$$
$$58 = (11 \times 5) + 3$$
$$5 = (1 \times 3) + 2$$
$$3 = (1 \times 2) + 1$$
$$2 = (1 \times 1) + 1$$
$$1 = (1 \times 1) + 0.$$

In this case the GCD is 1. But since 1 divides every integer, we say that 7655 and 1001 are **relatively prime,** meaning that they have no common divisors other than one

Finally, we consider the case of the GCD of three numbers. Suppose we wish to find the GCD of 45, 72 and 105. We already know that the GCD of 45 and 72 is 9. Hence we proceed as follows:

$$105 = (11 \times 9) + 6$$
$$9 = (1 \times 6) + 3$$
$$6 = (2 \times 3) + 0.$$

Thus the GCD of 105 and 9 is 3. From this we conclude that the GCD of 45, 72 and 105 is 3. We make practical use of this knowledge in factoring. For example,

$$45 + 72 + 105 = 3 \times (15 + 24 + 35)$$
$$= 3 \times (15 + 35 + 24)$$
$$= 3 \times (50 + 24)$$
$$= 3 \times 74.$$

## 3. Least common multiple

Another useful concept is that of **least common multiple** (LCM). Starting with any number, say 4, the numbers 4, 8, 12, 16, 20, 24, etc. are called *multiples* of 4. Suppose we wish to add the two fractions $\frac{3}{8}$ and $\frac{5}{14}$. We need the least common multiple of 8 and 14. We now list multiples of 8 and 14:

| Multiples of 8 | Multiples of 14 |
| --- | --- |
| 8 | 14 |
| 16 | 28 |
| 24 | 42 |
| 32 | 56 |
| 40 | 70 |
| 48 | 84 |
| 56 | 98 |
| 64 | 112 |
| 72 | 126 |

| Multiples of 8 | Multiples of 14 |
|:---:|:---:|
| 80 | 140 |
| 88 | . |
| 96 | . |
| 104 | . |
| 112 | . |
| . | |
| . | |

Of these, 56 and 112 are called *common* multiples of 8 and 14 since they appear in *both* columns. But 56 is the smallest of the common multiples, hence 56 is the least common multiple. Knowing this number, we can proceed to add the two fractions ⅜ and 5⁄14 as follows:

$$\frac{3}{8} + \frac{5}{14} = \left(\frac{3}{8} \times 1\right) + \left(\frac{5}{14} \times 1\right) \qquad \text{(multiplicative identity)}$$

$$= \left(\frac{3}{8} \times \frac{7}{7}\right) + \left(\frac{5}{14} \times \frac{4}{4}\right) \qquad \text{(multiplicative identity and LCM)}$$

$$= \frac{21}{56} + \frac{20}{56} \qquad \text{(multiplication of rational numbers)}$$

$$= (21 + 20) \times \frac{1}{56} \qquad \text{(distributive property)}$$

$$= 41 \times \frac{1}{56} \qquad \text{(addition)}$$

$$= \frac{41}{56} \qquad \text{(multiplication of rational numbers).}$$

Note that we have not said anything about "least common denominator" or "only like things can be added" but have used only the properties of numbers.

An alternate way of performing the above addition is the following:

$$\frac{3}{8} + \frac{5}{14} = \left(\frac{3}{8} \times 1\right) + \left(\frac{5}{14} \times 1\right)$$

$$= \left(\frac{3}{8} \times \frac{14}{14}\right) + \left(\frac{5}{14} \times \frac{8}{8}\right)$$

$$= \frac{42}{112} + \frac{40}{112}$$

$$= (42 + 40) \times \frac{1}{112}$$

$$= 82 \times \frac{1}{112}$$

$$= \frac{82}{112}$$

$$= \frac{82}{112} \div \frac{2}{2}$$

$$= \frac{41}{56}.$$

This again uses only the properties of numbers but does not use the idea of LCM. This method may be preferable with slow students.

In Chapter 4 we factored numbers into their prime factors by using factor trees. We noted the excellent drill provided by this activity—drill which was also fun.

We do not make factor trees just for fun or just for drill, however. They have a practical value which can be appreciated as soon as the student has to add rational numbers. Consider the addition example,

$$\frac{5}{36} + \frac{9}{48}.$$

The problem here is to find the LCM of 36 and 48. This is often referred to as the "least common denominator." We begin by making factor trees for 36 and 48.

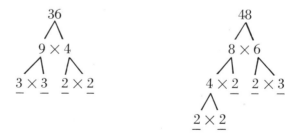

Next we examine the prime factors (underlined) and see that only the numbers 2 and 3 are involved. Finally, we take the product

$$2 \times 2 \times 2 \times 2 \times 3 \times 3$$

as the LCM of 36 and 48. We have taken *four* twos because there were four in the final factoring of 48 and only two in 36. We took *two* threes because there were two in the factoring of 36 and only one in 48. In other words, we take the *maximum* number of factors that appear in the factoring of any *one* number.

Knowing that the LCM of 36 and 48 is $2 \times 2 \times 2 \times 2 \times 3 \times 3$ or 144, we now transform the addition of $5/36$ and $9/48$ into the following:

$$\left(\frac{5}{36} \times \frac{4}{4}\right) + \left(\frac{9}{48} \times \frac{3}{3}\right) = \frac{20}{144} + \frac{27}{144}$$

$$= \frac{1}{144} \times (20 + 27)$$

$$= \frac{1}{144} \times 47$$

$$= \frac{47}{144}.$$

Since 47 is a prime number, it is not possible to reduce this last fraction to lowest terms. Why?

## 4. The octal system of numeration—base 8

We have studied the quinary (base 5) system of numeration in Chapter 4 and contrasted it with the decimal system. In the decimal system we use ten digits,

$$0, 1, 2, 3, 4, 5, 6, 7, 8, 9$$

and place values are powers of ten. For example, 3279 means

$$(3 \times 10^3) + (2 \times 10^2) + (7 \times 10) + (9 \times 1).$$

In the quinary system we use five digits,

$$0, 1, 2, 3, 4$$

and place values are powers of five. For example, $(4302)_5$ means

$$(4 \times 5^3) + (3 \times 5^2) + (0 \times 5) + (2 \times 1).$$

In order to fix these ideas we consider another system of numeration.

The **octal system** of numeration (base 8) is especially important because this is the system that is used in some modern electronic computers. In the octal system we use eight digits,

$$0, 1, 2, 3, 4, 5, 6, 7$$

and place values are powers of eight. A typical numeral in the octal system would be $(37650)_8$. This becomes in expanded notation

$$
\begin{aligned}
(37650)_8 &= (3 \times 8^4) + (7 \times 8^3) + (6 \times 8^2) + (5 \times 8) + (0 \times 1) \\
&= (3 \times 4096) + (7 \times 512) + (6 \times 64) + (5 \times 8) + (0 \times 1) \\
&= 12\,288 + 3584 + 384 + 40 + 0 \\
&= (16296)_{10}.
\end{aligned}
$$

Note that all the calculations on the right of the equality are done in the decimal system. We say that 37650 in the octal system is the same as 16296 in the decimal system, that is,

$$(37650)_8 = (16296)_{10}.$$

Knowing the place values in the octal system—1, 8, 64, 512, 4096, and so on (from right to left) we can also change a decimal numeral to an octal numeral. Suppose we wish to write 1965 in octal notation. The question is how many 4096's, 512's, 64's, 8's, 1's we can find in 1965. Obviously, there are no 4096's in 1965. But there are three 512's. However, three 512's are 1536 so that $1965 - 1536 = 429$ is still left. Now there are six 64's in 429. But, again six 64's are 384 so that $429 - 384 = 45$ is left. There are five 8's in 45 and five 1's. Thus

$$(1965)_{10} = (3 \times 512) + (6 \times 64) + (5 \times 8) + (5 \times 1)$$

which means,

$$(1965)_{10} = (3655)_8.$$

An equivalent (and much easier!) way to arrive at this result is to divide 1965 by 8 over and over, keeping track of the *remainder* each time. We have

$$
\begin{array}{r|rl}
8 & 1965 & \\
8 & 245 & 5 \\
8 & 30 & 5 \\
& 3 & 6 \\
\end{array}
$$

The remainders together with the last quotient produce 3655 which is the octal equivalent of 1965. Note that the "trick" here is that 1965 was divided by 8 three times and the quotient was 3. But dividing by 8 three times is the same as dividing by 512. In either case we obtained a 3 in the 512's place.

Computations in the octal system are made more easily if we make use of addition and multiplication tables.

| + | 0 | 1 | 2 | 3 | 4 | 5 | 6 | 7 |
|---|---|---|---|---|---|---|---|---|
| 0 | 0 | 1 | 2 | 3 | 4 | 5 | 6 | 7 |
| 1 | 1 | 2 | 3 | 4 | 5 | 6 | 7 | 10 |
| 2 | 2 | 3 | 4 | 5 | 6 | 7 | 10 | 11 |
| 3 | 3 | 4 | 5 | 6 | 7 | 10 | 11 | 12 |
| 4 | 4 | 5 | 6 | 7 | 10 | 11 | 12 | 13 |
| 5 | 5 | 6 | 7 | 10 | 11 | 12 | 13 | 14 |
| 6 | 6 | 7 | 10 | 11 | 12 | 13 | 14 | 15 |
| 7 | 7 | 10 | 11 | 12 | 13 | 14 | 15 | 16 |

| × | 0 | 1 | 2 | 3 | 4 | 5 | 6 | 7 |
|---|---|---|---|---|---|---|---|---|
| 0 | 0 | 0 | 0 | 0 | 0 | 0 | 0 | 0 |
| 1 | 0 | 1 | 2 | 3 | 4 | 5 | 6 | 7 |
| 2 | 0 | 2 | 4 | 6 | 10 | 12 | 14 | 16 |
| 3 | 0 | 3 | 6 | 11 | 14 | 17 | 22 | 25 |
| 4 | 0 | 4 | 10 | 14 | 20 | 24 | 30 | 34 |
| 5 | 0 | 5 | 12 | 17 | 24 | 31 | 36 | 43 |
| 6 | 0 | 6 | 14 | 22 | 30 | 36 | 44 | 52 |
| 7 | 0 | 7 | 16 | 25 | 34 | 43 | 52 | 61 |

With the aid of these tables it is quite simple to do addition, subtraction and multiplication in the octal system. Division is a bit more complicated but can be done also.

## 5. The binary system of numeration—base 2

Many computers use the **binary system** of numeration (base 2) because this is the most simple of all numeration systems. In the binary system we have only two digits, 0 and 1, and place values are powers of two. A system of numeration that has only two digits has many possibilities; for instance zero can be represented by an open circuit in the computer and one by a closed circuit. Or, the digit one can be represented by a *hole* in a card and zero by *no hole* in a card.

Arithmetic in the binary system is ridiculously simple as shown by the following addition and multiplication tables:

| + | 0 | 1 |
|---|---|---|
| 0 | 0 | 1 |
| 1 | 1 | 10 |

| × | 0 | 1 |
|---|---|---|
| 0 | 0 | 0 |
| 1 | 0 | 1 |

Compare these with the addition and multiplication facts that must be learned in the decimal system! Strangly enough, however, this simplicity is, in itself, difficult!

A typical numeral in the binary system would be 10110111. Note that *only* zeros and ones can be used. The decimal equivalent of this numeral can be found by considering the proper place values. For example,

$$(10110111)_2 = (1 \times 2^7) + (0 \times 2^6) + (1 \times 2^5) + (1 \times 2^4)$$
$$+ (0 \times 2^3) + (1 \times 2^2) + (1 \times 2) + (1 \times 1)$$
$$= 128 + 0 + 32 + 16 + 0 + 4 + 2 + 1$$
$$= (183)_{10}.$$

Hence $(10110111)_2 = (183)_{10}$. Conversely,

```
2 | 183
2 |  91   1  ↑
2 |  45   1
2 |  22   1
2 |  11   0
2 |   5   1
2 |   2   1
        1   0
```

Thus $(183)_{10} = (10110111)_2$.

Working with number systems other than the decimal is interesting, it provides valuable drill in a subtle way, and it gives a deeper appreciation of the decimal system. Add to this the fact that number systems other than the decimal are currently being used in computers, and you can see the importance of this topic.

Unfortunately, there is only one way to gain an understanding of other systems of numeration. It is necessary to practice, that is, to do arithmetic problems. In this respect mathematics is very similar to learning to play the violin. One can listen to a violin teacher while he explains the techniques of bowing and fingering. One can watch him and listen to him as he plays the assigned lesson. But in order to acquire any degree of skill one must practice—long and often. So it is with mathematics. It is not enough to *read* about it. It is not enough to *watch* the teacher as he converts an octal or binary numeral to a decimal numeral. The student must *do* these things himself, however difficult it seems to be at first. There is no easy road to success in mathematics!

The exercises at the end of this chapter are more numerous than they have been until now. They should provide the student with the necessary practice.

## Exercises 8B

1. Find all the prime factors of (a) 256   (b) 243   (c) 245   (d) 5040   (e) 1964.

2. Find all the divisors of (a) 240   (b) 1024   (c) 1066   (d) 4158   (e) 1800.

3. What is the greatest common divisor of (a) 45 and 63   (b) 378 and 441   (c) 935 and 1105   (d) 624 and 1019?

4. What is the greatest common divisor of (a) 14, 35, and 55   (b) 365, 146, and 405?

5. Find the least common multiple of (a) 12 and 15   (b) 9 and 7   (c) 11 and 13   (d) 6 and 16.

6. Convert the following decimal numerals to octal. (a) 963   (b) 27   (c) 1099   (d) 6987.

7. Convert the following octal numerals to decimal. (a) 17   (b) 367   (c) 1077   (d) 20453.

**8.** Perform the following arithmetic in the octal system: (a) $56 + 72$ (b) $65 - 47$ (c) $36 \times 45$ (d) $140 \div 4$. (Note—all numerals are given *in the octal system*).

**9.** Convert 765 in the octal system to the quinary system. (Hint—go by way of the decimal system).

**10.** What is $(36\ 798)_{10}$ in the octal system?

**11.** Convert the following binary numerals to decimal. (a) 1011 (b) 111101 (c) 1010111 (d) 11100111.

**12.** Convert the following decimal numerals to binary. (a) 125 (b) 67 (c) 389 (d) 2098.

**13.** Perform the following arithmetic in the binary system:
(a) $1011 + 1001$ (b) $11111 + 101$ (c) $1101 - 111$
(d) $10101 - 1010$ (e) $101 \times 111$ (f) $1101 \times 110$
(g) $1001000 \div 1000$.
(Note—all numerals are given *in the binary system*).

**14.** Convert $(1101101)_2$ to (a) the octal system (b) the quinary system (c) the decimal system.

**15.** Convert $(7065)_8$ to (a) the binary system (b) the quinary system (c) the decimal system.

**16.** Compute $(365)_{10} - (110110)_2$.

**17.** What is $(265)_8 + (1011101)_2$?

**18.** Find the sum of $(375)_8$ and $(1011)_2$.

**19.** What is $(36)_8 \times (1101)_2$?

**20.** Find a way of converting an octal numeral to a binary numeral directly without going through the decimal system.

# 9/Sets (C)

## 1. Complementation, a unary operation

We have discussed two binary operations that are used in connection with sets—forming the union and forming the intersection. There is also a *unary* operation that can be applied to sets. A **unary** operation is an operation that can be applied to *one* quantity to yield a similar quantity. For example, finding the square root of a number is a unary operation because when applied to the single number 36, it yields the single number 6.

One unary operation that we use with sets is called **complementation** or forming the **complement.** It is denoted by a prime (′) and $A'$ means: all those elements of $U$ (the universe of discourse) which are *not* elements of $A$. In terms of a Venn diagram (Figure 9.1), the shaded portion denotes $A'$. As before, we indicate the universe of discourse $U$ by a rectangle and the set $A$ by some arbitrary configuration.

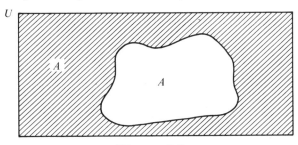

**Figure 9.1**

In mathematics the idea of a complement is a very useful one. Although complementation appears to be a *negative* idea ($A'$ means that which is *not* in $A$) it happens that very often, when we do not know what the answer *is*, it is useful to know what it *isn't*. This allows us to get at the true answer using a negative approach in many cases. For example, if I tell you that a certain counting number cannot be more than 9 and cannot be less than 7, you will have no difficulty in reaching the conclusion that this counting number must be 7, 8, or 9. You should also realize at this point that the universe of discourse $U$ and the empty set $\emptyset$ are related as follows:

$$U' = \emptyset$$
$$\emptyset' = U.$$

For any set $A$, we have the relations

$$A \cap A' = \emptyset$$
$$A \cup A' = U.$$

For any set $A$ whatever, it is true that

$$(A')' = A.$$

To *prove* this result in a rigorous manner we would reason as follows: any element that belongs to $(A')'$ *cannot* belong to $A'$ (Why?). Hence such an element *must* belong to $A$. But this shows that $(A')'$ is a subset of $A$, that is, $(A')' \subseteq A$.

On the other hand, if an element belongs to $A$, then it *cannot* belong to $A'$. (Why?). Hence it *must* belong to $(A')'$ (Why?). In other words, an element that belongs to $A$, also belongs to $(A')'$. But this shows that $A$ is a subset of $(A')'$, that is, $A \subseteq (A')'$. Recalling the definition of subset, we are forced to the inevitable conclusion that $A = (A')'$.

If you can follow the above reasoning, you are capable of understanding and doing genuine mathematics. Notice how many times we applied *deductive reasoning* (if-then reasoning) in the above argument. This is the very essence, the very soul of mathematics. *If* you can get even a glimmer of this, *then* you are on your way to an understanding of mathematics.

Using the set of counting numbers $N$, we can give an example of complementation. Let

$$A = \{n \mid n > 7\}$$

and

$$B = \{n \mid n \leq 6\},$$

then

$$(A \cup B)' = \{7\}$$

and

$$(A \cap B)' = N.$$

The statement

$$A = \{n \mid n > 7\}$$

is read, "$A$ is the set whose elements are $n$ where $n > 7$." The vertical line means "where" or "such that." In all cases, of course, the universe of discourse must be specified.

## 2. De Morgan's laws

By restricting our universe of discourse so that

$$U = \{1, 2, 3, \ldots, 10\},$$

let

$$A = \{3, 4, 7, 8\}$$

and

$$B = \{5, 7, 9\}.$$

Then

$$A \cup B = \{3, 4, 5, 7, 8, 9\}$$

and

$$(A \cup B)' = \{1, 2, 6, 10\}.$$

On the other hand,

$$A' = \{1, 2, 5, 6, 9, 10\}$$

and

$$B' = \{1, 2, 3, 4, 6, 8, 10\}$$

so that

$$A' \cap B' = \{1, 2, 6, 10\}.$$

**Sets (C)**                                                                 127

We have shown that

$$(A \cup B)' = A' \cap B'. \qquad (9.1)$$

The reader should show in a similar manner that

$$(A \cap B)' = A' \cup B'. \qquad (9.2)$$

Equations (9.1) and (9.2) are *special cases* of relations between sets which are *generally* true. These relations are known as De Morgan's laws.[1] Stated in words, Eq. (9.1) would be, "The complement of the union of two sets is the intersection of their complements," while Eq. (9.2) would be, "The complement of the intersection of two sets is the union of their complements." Notice that the two statements differ only in that the words "union" and "intersection" are interchanged.

We should mention here that we recommend very strongly that the student at all levels form the habit of translating mathematical symbols into words. Without doing this, mathematics will continue to be mysterious.

## 3. Properties of set operations

There are a number of other properties of union and intersection which are worth considering. These properties can be checked by means of Venn diagrams using colored pencils or numbered regions. They may also be proved rigorously. We shall give examples of both methods.

An obvious property of union and intersection is given by the following where $A$ and $B$ are arbitrary sets:

$$A \cup B = B \cup A \quad \text{and} \quad A \cap B = B \cap A. \qquad (9.3)$$

In words, forming the union and forming the intersection of two sets are commutative operations—the result does not depend on the order in which the sets are taken.[2]

The question arises how to form the union of *more than two* sets

[1] Augustus De Morgan (1806–1871) was a mathematician of considerable talent, an excellent and influential teacher, and an ardent collector of paradoxes, puzzles and riddles.

[2] Recall that addition and multiplication of rational numbers also have this property, i.e., $a + b = b + a$ and $a \times b = b \times a$.

since forming the union is a binary operation. In other words, how do we form the set designated by $A \cup B \cup C$? There are two different ways to proceed—one can form $A \cup B$ and then form the union of this and $C$, or one can form $B \cup C$ and then form the union of $A$ and this. In symbols the two methods are given by $(A \cup B) \cup C$ and $A \cup (B \cup C)$. We will show how these may be examined with a Venn diagram.

Consider the three sets $A$, $B$, and $C$ shown in Figure 9.2. We have

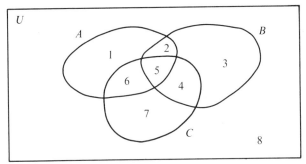

**Figure 9.2**

numbered the regions so that we can refer to them easily. Coloring the regions serves the same purpose and may be preferable with young children.

$(A \cup B)$ consists of regions 1, 2, 3, 4, 5, and 6, hence $(A \cup B) \cup C$ consists of regions 1, 2, 3, 4, 5, 6, and 7.

$(B \cup C)$ consists of regions 2, 3, 4, 5, 6, and 7, hence $A \cup (B \cup C)$ consists of regions 1, 2, 3, 4, 5, 6, and 7. Thus in this case,

$$(A \cup B) \cup C = A \cup (B \cup C). \tag{9.4}$$

It can be proved that Eq. (9.4) holds for any arbitrary sets, that is, finding the union of sets is *associative*. The student should show that

$$(A \cap B) \cap C = A \cap (B \cap C). \tag{9.5}$$

Hint: The left side consists of region 5.[3]

We may use the last figure to illustrate one of De Morgan's laws, say Eq. (9.2). The set $A \cap B$ consists of regions 2 and 5, hence $(A \cap B)'$

[3] Again we have analogies to Eqs. (9.4) and (9.5) in the addition and multiplication of rational numbers, $(a + b) + c = a + (b + c)$ and $(a \times b) \times c = a \times (b \times c)$.

consists of regions 1, 3, 4, 6, 7, and 8. On the other hand, $A'$ consists of regions 3, 4, 7, and 8 and $B'$ consists of regions 1, 6, 7, and 8. Thus $A' \cup B'$ consists of regions 1, 3, 4, 6, 7, and 8 just as $(A \cap B)'$ does.

The pedant may object that the above reasoning depends on how the sets are drawn. This is true and hence a "proof" like above cannot be wholly general. It is instructive, however, for young children to draw their diagrams in *different* ways and yet arrive at the *same* conclusion. This process strengthens their belief that Equations (9.1), (9.2), (9.3), and (9.4) are *generally* true. The rigorous proofs will have to be postponed until later.

So far we have seen that the operations $\cup$ and $\cap$ on sets have many of the same characteristics as the operations $+$ and $\times$ on rational numbers. It may be worthwhile to compare the two situations.

|  |  |
|---|---|
| **Union of Sets** | **Addition of Rational Numbers** |
| **1.** $A \cup B$ is a set | $a + b$ is a rational number |
| (closure property) | |
| **2.** $A \cup B = B \cup A$ | $a + b = b + a$ |
| (commutative property) | |
| **3.** $(A \cup B) \cup C = A \cup (B \cup C)$ | $(a + b) + c = a + (b + c)$ |
| (associative property) | |
| **4.** $A \cup \varnothing = A$ | $a + 0 = a$ |
| (identity) | |

Note the similarity between properties A1 to A4 inclusive given earlier for rational numbers and numbers 1 to 4 inclusive above.

Continuing in this same vein we compare intersection of sets and multiplication of rational numbers.

|  |  |
|---|---|
| **Intersection of Sets** | **Multiplication of Rational Numbers** |
| **1.** $A \cap B$ is a set | $a \times b$ is a rational number |
| (closure property) | |
| **2.** $A \cap B = B \cap A$ | $a \times b = b \times a$ |
| (commutative property) | |

**3.** $(A \cap B) \cap C = A \cap (B \cap C)$ $\qquad$ $(a \times b) \times c = a \times (b \times c)$

(associative property)

**4.** $A \cap U = A$ $\qquad\qquad\qquad\qquad$ $a \times 1 = a$

(identity)

Again note the similarity between properties **M1** to **M4** given earlier for rational numbers and numbers **1** to **4** inclusive above.

It seems reasonable to ask if there are any other properties that sets and rational numbers have in common. For example, is there a property of sets analogous to the distributive property? Recall that for rational numbers $a$, $b$, and $c$, it was true that

$$a \times (b + c) = (a \times b) + (a \times c).$$

Is it also true that

$$A \cap (B \cup C) = (A \cap B) \cup (A \cap C)?$$

We prove that this is true in a rigorous manner.

Let $x$ be any element whatsoever that belongs to the set $A \cap (B \cup C)$. Then $x$ belongs to $A$ *and* also to $B \cup C$. (Why?) Since $x$ belongs to $B \cup C$, it belongs to either $B$ or $C$. If $x$ belongs to $B$, then it belongs to $A \cap B$. If $x$ belongs to $C$, then it belongs to $A \cap C$. Thus, in any event, $x$ belongs to $(A \cap B) \cup (A \cap C)$. In other words, any element that belongs to the set $A \cap (B \cup C)$ also belongs to the set $(A \cap B) \cup (A \cap C)$. This proves that $A \cap (B \cup C) \subseteq (A \cap B) \cup (A \cap C)$. (Why?)

Now suppose $y$ is any element whatsoever that belongs to the set $(A \cap B) \cup (A \cap C)$. This means that either $y$ belongs to $A \cap B$ *or* it belongs to $A \cap C$. In any event, $y$ belongs to the set $A$. (Why?) But $y$ also belongs either to $B$ or $C$. (Why?) Hence $y$ belongs to $A \cap (B \cup C)$. In other words, any element that belongs to the set $(A \cap B) \cup (A \cap C)$ also belongs to the set $A \cap (B \cup C)$. This proves that $(A \cap B) \cup (A \cap C) \subseteq A \cap (B \cup C)$. Thus the two sets in question—$(A \cap B) \cup (A \cap C)$ and $A \cap (B \cup C)$—are equal since each is a subset of the other. This proves the distributive property

$$A \cap (B \cup C) = (A \cap B) \cup (A \cap C) \qquad (9.6)$$

which is analogous to property **D** for rational numbers,

$$a \times (b + c) = (a \times b) + (a \times c).$$

The student can also show that the operations $\cap$ and $\cup$ in Eq. (9.6) may be interchanged. In other words, it is also true that

$$A \cup (B \cap C) = (A \cup B) \cap (A \cup C). \tag{9.7}$$

The analogous result for rational numbers is not true. For example,

$$3 + (4 \times 5) \neq (3 + 4) \times (3 + 5).$$

For nonzero rational numbers $a$ we also had

$$a \times a^{-1} = 1$$

where $a^{-1}$ is the *multiplicative inverse* (also called the *reciprocal*) of $a$. For sets we have

$$A \cup A' = U. \tag{9.8}$$

We hasten to point out that the binary operations $\cup$ and $+$ as well as $\cap$ and $\times$ are not the same, nor are they equivalent in any way. It just happens, however, that there is a similarity—or analogy—between the properties for sets and those for rational numbers. This analogy is not complete as shown by the last examples.

The similarities are pointed out so that the reader's understanding will be strengthened and so that he may have some practice in abstract thinking.

## 4. The Cartesian product of two sets

We introduce the concept of *Cartesian product* with a problem which might be called a "wardrobe problem." Susan's wardrobe contains four blouses whose colors are coral, tan, white, and yellow. She also has three jumpers whose colors are green, plaid and red. Susan has no difficulty calculating that this gives her 12 different combinations or outfits.[4]

From a logical viewpoint, however, there *is* difficulty in arriving at the number 12. Are we to multiply 4 *blouses* by 3 *jumpers* and get 12 *combinations* for an answer? This is certainly *not* in accord with the careful, systematic development which is a feature of the "new mathematics."

[4] We apologize if any of the color combinations should offend the reader's aesthetic sense. Remember, this is only a hypothetical example!

To get around this difficulty we use a concept called "the Cartesian[5] product" of two sets. Let us denote the set of Susan's blouses by $B$, that is,

$$B = \{c, t, w, y\}$$

and the set of her jumpers by $J$, that is,

$$J = \{g, p, r\}.$$

The **Cartesian product** of $B$ and $J$ is denoted by $B \times J$ and is defined as the following set:

$$B \times J = \{(c, g), (c, p), (c, r), (t, g), (t, p), (t, r),$$
$$(w, g), (w, p), (w, r), (y, g), (y, p), (y, r)\}.$$

In other words, the elements of the set $B \times J$ are all possible *ordered pairs* such that the *first* member of the pair belongs to set $B$ and the *second* to set $J$. Each ordered pair is actually a combination in Susan's wardrobe. For example, the pair $(t, g)$ is a combination of a tan blouse and a green jumper. It would be incorrect to write this as $(g, t)$ since this indicates a green blouse and a tan jumper, which is not one of the possible combinations. This is where the "ordering" comes in. In general,

$$B \times J \neq J \times B$$

for sets $B$ and $J$, that is, the Cartesian product of sets does *not* have the commutative property.

It can be proved that $n(B \times J) = n(B) \times n(J)$, where the notation $n(B)$ means "the number of elements in the set B." Some educators believe that this is the way multiplication should be defined because *all* situations can be explained by *one* method. We feel that defining multiplication as repeated addition is more reasonable for the early grades. It is very unlikely that problems like the "wardrobe problem" will arise and that pupils will ask, "how is it possible to add four blouses three jumpers times?" We do feel, however, that the teacher should be aware of the logical difficulty encountered here.

[5] Named after René Descartes (1596–1650), a French mathematician and philosopher who first wrote about analytic geometry—a "union" of algebra and geometry. The Latin equivalent of Descartes is Cartesius and this was the name he used since Latin was the universal scientific language of his day.

# 5. Cardinal numbers

When we talked about sets in Chapter 5 we were also interested in the *number of elements* in the set. We used the notation $n(A)$ to denote the number of elements in $A$. The number of elements in a *finite* set is always a whole number and we can make certain statements about this number.

For example, let

$$A = \{3, 6, 9, 12, 15, 18\}$$

and

$$B = \{2, 4, 6, 8, 10\}.$$

Then $n(A) = 6$, $n(B) = 5$, and we have

$$n(A) > n(B).$$

We can also say

$$n(A \cup B) = 10$$

since

$$A \cup B = \{2, 3, 4, 6, 8, 9, 10, 12, 15, 18\}.$$

This can be generalized as follows:

$$n(A \cup B) \leq n(A) + n(B).$$

In fact, we can go one step further and state

$$n(A \cup B) = n(A) + n(B) - n(A \cap B).$$

This last is a general statement that is true for any sets $A$ and $B$ whatever.

We call your attention to the fact that it is not possible to make such a precise statement about $A \cap B$. The intersection of two sets may be the empty set, or it may be either one of the sets.

It is very important to know the number of elements in a set, since in a way this characterizes the set. The number of elements in a set is called the **cardinal number** of the set. As we count the number of elements in a finite set, the *last* number we say is the *cardinal number* of the set.

To further clarify this concept and to distinguish between cardinal and *ordinal* numbers, consider the three sets

$$C = \{4, 3, 1, 2\}$$
$$D = \{1, 3, 5, 7\}$$
$$E = \{2, 1, 3, 6\}.$$

The number 4 is the *first* element of set $C$, the number 3 is the *second* element of sets $C$ and $D$, etc. The numbers *first* and *second* are **ordinal** numbers. All three sets are described by the cardinal number 4; all three sets have the cardinal number 4. Thus the cardinal number tells how many elements there are in a set and an ordinal number tells how (in what order) the elements are arranged. Finally, the cardinal number of the empty set is zero.

In case a set has an infinite number of elements, we cannot arrive at the cardinal number by counting. For infinite sets Georg Cantor[6] has established another criterion. Using the set

$$N = \{1, 2, 3, 4, 5, \ldots\}$$

we say an infinite set $E$ *is equivalent to* $N$ (written $E \approx N$) if the elements of $E$ can be put into one-to-one correspondence with the elements of $N$. This idea is not limited to infinite sets and we can say

$$C \approx D \approx E$$

for the sets previously mentioned. For finite sets $C$ and $D$, saying

$$C \approx D$$

is the same as saying

$$n(C) = n(D),$$

and we do not seem to have gained anything but a new symbol. When dealing with infinite sets, however, the concept of equivalence is important.

Consider the set of even numbers,

$$E = \{0, 2, 4, 6, 8, \ldots\},$$

[6] Georg Cantor (1845–1918) in the years 1871–84 created a completely new and very special mathematical discipline, the theory of sets, in which was founded a theory of infinity with all the incisiveness of modern mathematics.

the set of odd numbers,

$$F = \{1, 3, 5, 7, 9, \ldots\},$$

and the set of "thousands,"

$$T = \{1000, 2000, 3000, 4000, \ldots\}.$$

Each of the sets $E$, $F$ and $T$ can be put into one-to-one correspondence with the set of natural numbers $N$. Hence it is logical that the same cardinal number be used to designate the sets $E$, $F$, $T$ and $N$. It was Cantor who suggested that this cardinal number be designated by $\aleph_0$ (read "aleph null"). Aleph is the first letter of the Hebrew alphabet and the zero subscript is used to indicate that this is the *lowest order* of infinity. The set of irrational numbers has a cardinal number which is a higher order of infinity than the set of rational numbers. It can be shown that the set $R$ of rational numbers has cardinal number $\aleph_0$.

Dealing with infinite sets is tricky and it is essential to use the concept of equivalence in order to prevent paradoxes. For example, it does not seem possible that there can be as many even numbers as there are counting numbers or as many elements in a set like $T$ as in $N$. Yet, the process of matching or one-to-one correspondence leads us to this conclusion.

The idea of infinity has so long been a philosophical one that it is difficult for some people to comprehend it mathematically. Bertrand Russell, the philosopher, has described the paradox of Tristram Shandy.[7] Russell says,

Tristram Shandy, as we know, employed two years in chronicling the first two days of his life, and lamented that, at this rate, material would accumulate faster than he could deal with it, so that, as years went by, he would be farther and farther from the end of his history. Now I maintain that, if he had lived for ever, and had not wearied of his task, then, even if his life had continued as eventfully as it began, no part of his biography would have remained unwritten. For consider: the hundredth day will be described in the hundredth year, the thousandth in the thousandth year, and so on. Whatever day we may choose as so far on that he cannot hope to reach it, that day will be described in the corresponding year. Thus any day that may

[7] Russell, Bertrand: "Mathematics and the Metaphysicians." In "The World of Mathematics" edited by James R. Newman, Simon and Schuster, New York, vol. 3, 1956, p. 1586. This originally appeared in Russell's "Mysticism and Logic," Allen and Unwin, Ltd.

be mentioned will be written up sooner or later, and therefore no part of the biography will remain permanently unwritten. This paradoxical but perfectly true proposition depends upon the fact that the number of days in all time is no greater than the number of years.

Infinite sets have a number of strange properties. Consider the sets

$$N = \{1, 2, 3, 4, 5, 6, \ldots\}$$

and

$$H = \{4, 6, 8, 10, \ldots\}.$$

Notice that $H$ is like the previously defined set $E$ with the first two elements omitted. In spite of this omission, however, we can still match elements of $N$ with those of $H$. In fact, to 1 corresponds 4, to 2 corresponds 6, to 3 corresponds 8, . . . , to 100 corresponds 202, and, in general, to $n$ corresponds $2n + 2$. Thus we have a one-to-one correspondence between $N$ and $H$, that is,

$$H \approx N.$$

We call attention to the fact that instead of forming $H$ by deleting the first two elements of $E$, we could have deleted the first hundred elements or the first million or any finite number. Thus we have another characteristic of an infinite set, namely, that it is equivalent to a subset of itself. A slightly modified version of this idea can be used to give a definition of an infinite set: a set is infinite if it is equivalent to a *proper* subset of itself. The modification consists of inserting the word "proper." Recall the definition of a subset: $A$ is a subset of $B$ if every element of $A$ is also an element of $B$. According to this definition every set is a subset of itself. Hence we need the idea of a "proper subset": a set $A$ is a **proper subset** of $B$ if every element of $A$ is also an element of $B$ *and* if there is at least one element in $B$ which is not in $A$. In symbols, $A \subset B$, that is, $A$ is a proper subset of $B$.

Note that saying, "a set is infinite if it is equivalent to a subset of itself" implies that *every* set is infinite. (Why?) The addition of the word "proper" clarifies the matter. In mathematics definitions are extremely important and part of our modern approach is to pay more attention to them. We make a positive effort to say what we mean and mean what we say at all times.

Finally, we point out that a finite set is defined to be one that is *not infinite*. Since the latter has been carefully defined, the negative of this definition is equally valid. To appreciate both definitions, we suggest you try to make a one-to-one correspondence between a finite set and one of its proper subsets.

## Exercises 9C

1. If $U = R$ (the set of rational numbers) and $A = \{n \mid n \geq 7\}$, find $A'$.

2. If $U = R$ and $B = \{n \mid 3 < n \leq 8\}$, find $B'$.

3. Using $A$ and $B$ as defined in exercises 1 and 2, find (a) $A \cup B$ (b) $A \cap B$ (c) $(A \cup B)'$ (d) $(A \cap B)'$ (e) $A' \cup B'$ (f) $A' \cap B'$.

4. Using $A$ and $B$ as defined in exercises 1 and 2, find (a) $(A \cup B) \cap B'$ (b) $(A \cap B) \cup A'$ (c) $(A \cup B)' \cup A'$ (d) $(A \cap B)' \cap B'$.

5. *Prove that $\varnothing' = U$.*

6. Using the sets $U$, $A$, and $B$ at the beginning of Section 2, show that $(A \cap B)' = A' \cup B'$.

7. Prove De Morgan's laws using a general Venn diagram.

8. Prove De Morgan's laws rigorously, that is, by the method used to prove that $(A')' = A$ in Section 1.

9. Prove that $A \cup (B \cap C) = (A \cup B) \cap (A \cup C)$ using a Venn diagram.

10. Repeat exercise 9 using a method of proof similar to the one in Section 3.

11. Given $A = \{1, 3\}$, $B = \{2, 3, 4\}$, find (a) $A \times B$ (b) $B \times A$.

12. Referring to exercise 11, find $(A \times B) \cap (B \times A)$.

13. What is the cardinal number of $E \cup F$, where $E = \{3, 6, 10, 5\}$ and $F = \{2, 8, 10, 12, 3\}$?

14. What is the cardinal number of $E \cap F$ with $E$ and $F$ defined as in exercise 13?

15. What is the cardinal number of the set
$$\{100, 101, 102, 103, 104, \ldots\}?$$

16. Prove that the sets $N$, $E$, $F$, and $T$ of Section 5 are equivalent. (Hint: what elements in $E$, $F$, and $T$ correspond to an arbitrary element $n$ of $N$?)

17. What is the cardinal number of $G \cap H$ where $G = \{3, 6, 9, 12, \ldots\}$ and $H = \{6, 12, 18, 24, \ldots\}$?

# 10/The Real Number System (C)

## 1. Negative numbers provide closure under subtraction

We need another concept to make our number system more complete. As yet, none of the sets so far discussed is closed under the operation of subtraction. Consider the number line we have been using so far.

We have seen that adding is the same as counting to the *right* and subtracting is the same as counting to the *left*. Thus to solve the problem of what number to assign to $4 - 6$ we need to give a name to the number two spaces to the left of zero. We call this number "negative two" and designate it $^-2$. We name the spaces to the left of zero $^-1, ^-2, ^-3, ^-4, \ldots$ from right to left. Numbers which are greater than zero are called **positive**, those that are less than zero are called **negative**. Zero, itself, is neither positive nor negative. In particular, the numbers $\ldots, ^-3, ^-2, ^-1, 0, 1, 2, 3, \ldots$ are called **integers.**

It is necessary to exercise reasonable care in working with both positive and negative numbers. For example, when *adding* negative numbers we count to the *left;* when *subtracting* we count to the *right.* Thus

$$^-4 + (^-2) = ^-6$$

and

$$^-4 - (^-2) = ^-2$$

as can be verified by counting properly on the number line. Similarly,

$$4 + (^-2) = ^-2$$

and

$$4 - (^-2) = 6$$

according to our convention about counting. Note that we do not give rules such as "two minuses make a plus" or "change the sign of the subtrahend and add" or any similar nonsense.

By admitting negative numbers to our number system, we not only have a system that is closed under subtraction but every number now has an *additive inverse*. The additive inverse of 2 is $^-2$, of $\frac{3}{4}$ is $^-\frac{3}{4}$, of $^-6$ is 6 etc. These additive inverses are also called **opposites.** They have the property that for any number $a$ and its additive inverse $^-a$,

**A5.** $a + (^-a) = 0$.

Now every rational number (except zero) has a multiplicative inverse and every rational number has an additive inverse.

Addition and subtraction present no difficulty, once we realize that on a complete number line (one on which both positive and negative numbers are marked) addition of *positive* numbers is the same as counting to the *right* and addition of *negative* numbers is the same as counting to the *left*. Since subtraction is the inverse of addition, it immediately follows that subtraction of *positive* numbers is the same as counting to the *left* and subtraction of *negative* numbers is the same as counting to the *right*.

Multiplication is a little more complicated, but we can easily handle the case $3 \times {}^-4$ because this is the same as $^-4 + {}^-4 + {}^-4$ and addition of negative numbers can be illustrated on the number line. Moreover, the problem of evaluating $3 \times {}^-4$ has a simple real-life analogy, namely, how much do you lose if you lose \$4 a day for 3 days? The answer, of course, is that you lose \$12.

It seems reasonable to expect the commutative property to hold for multiplication of negative numbers so that $^-4 \times 3$ is the same as $\cdot 3 \times {}^-4$, and this has already been defined.

We now come to the last big stumbling block, namely, what is $^-3 \times {}^-4$? There are a number of ways to attack this but, unfortunately, the number line does not help too much. This is understandable once we realize that the number line is a wonderful visual aid but we can't expect it to do miracles. It is impractical, for example, to use a number line to teach square root. All visual aids have limitations and the number line is no exception. Other visual aids also have limitations. For example, flash cards are extremely useful for teaching addition and multiplication facts but would hardly be considered for teaching philosophy.

In short, we are saying that the multiplication of a negative number by another negative number cannot be easily shown on a number line. There are other ways, however, to teach this idea and we give examples of some of them.

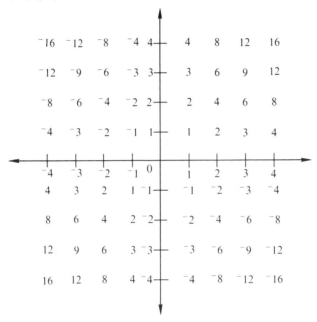

**Figure 10.1**

Many teachers prefer to use a grid in which the multiplication of various numbers is exhibited. Such a grid is made by taking two number lines perpendicular to each other, labelling the positive and negative numbers on both lines, and entering the products of the numbers in the appropriate places. A grid of this type is shown in Figure 10.1. The grid is to be interpreted as follows: if we go straight up from 3 and go straight across from 2, we will meet at a point marked

6—the product of 3 and 2. Similarly, the product of 3 and ⁻2 brings us to ⁻6, as does the product of 2 and ⁻3. The symmetry of the table shows that ⁻2 × ⁻3 is 6. If we start *below* the horizontal number line and follow one of the horizontal rows from right to left, we can see why it is natural for the entries to become positive when we cross the vertical number line. (Note that the products which fall on the two number lines are all zero.)

Another way to illustrate this idea is to take the case of a business man who realizes on Wednesday that he is losing $10 a day. This can be illustrated by a chart that shows ⁻10 for Thursday, ⁻20 for Friday, ⁻30 for Saturday, etc. The question is: what figures correspond to Tuesday and Monday? The following diagram shows the situation and indicates clearly that ⁻2 × ⁻10 = 20. Another way of expressing this is that if a man *loses* $10 a day what were his assets two days *ago?*

One more way to arrive at the correct answer is to consider the following expression:

$$(⁻2 × ⁻3) + (2 × ⁻3) + (2 × 3).$$

This is some number and, by using the properties of the real number system, we should be able to find its value. On the one hand, we have

$(⁻2 + 2) × ⁻3 + (2 × 3)$ by the distributive property,
$= (0 × ⁻3) + (2 × 3)$   by the property of opposites,
$= 0 + (2 × 3)$        by the annihilator property of zero
$= 2 × 3$            by the property of the additive identity.

On the other hand, we can also say

$(⁻2 × ⁻3) + 2 × (⁻3 + 3)$ by the distributive property,
$= (⁻2 × ⁻3) + 2 × 0$   as before,
$= (⁻2 × ⁻3) + 0$      as before,
$= ⁻2 × ⁻3$         as before.

Thus, in one case the expression is evaluated to $2 × 3$, and in the other case to $⁻2 × ⁻3$. The conclusion is inescapable: both of these must be equal, that is,

$$2 × 3 = ⁻2 × ⁻3.$$

While this proof is slightly sophisticated, it has the advantages that it is a strictly correct proof and that it can be generalized to show

$$a \times b = {}^-a \times {}^-b$$

for any real[1] numbers $a$ and $b$ whatever.

**Theorem.** $({}^-a) \times ({}^-b) = a \times b$ for rational numbers $a$ and $b$.

*Proof.*

1. Consider the following expression which, for the moment, is pulled out of a hat,

$$(a \times b) + [a \times ({}^-b)] + [({}^-a) \times ({}^-b)].$$

2. This can be written

$$a \times [b + ({}^-b)] + [({}^-a) \times ({}^-b)] \text{ by } \mathbf{D}.$$

3. Then this becomes

$$[a \times (0)] + [({}^-a) \times ({}^-b)] \text{ by } \mathbf{A5}.$$

4. And, by the annihilator property of zero,

$$0 + [({}^-a) \times ({}^-b)].$$

5. Finally, by **A4**, we have

$$({}^-a) \times ({}^-b).$$

6. Thus the expression we pulled out of a hat turns out to be the left side of the statement we are trying to prove.

7. Now someone else, just as familiar with the properties of the rational numbers as the one who obtained the result in step 5, could have written the expression in step 1 as

$$(a \times b) + [a + ({}^-a)] \times ({}^-b) \text{ by } \mathbf{D}.$$

8. Again, by **A5**, this becomes

$$(a \times b) + [0 \times ({}^-b)].$$

9. By the annihilator property of zero,

$$(a \times b) + 0.$$

[1] Real numbers arc discussed in Section 2.

10. Finally, by **A4**, we have

$$a \times b.$$

11. The very same expression that in step 5 was shown to be $(^-a) \times (^-b)$ is now shown in step 10 as $a \times b$. We are forced to the conclusion that these two are the same, that is,

$$(^-a) \times (^-b) = a \times b,$$

and this proves the theorem. Note that we used *only* the properties of the rational number system in proving the theorem. There was no hocus-pocus, and even our use of the expression *pulled out of a hat* is justified on the grounds that it was *the* expression needed to prove the theorem. Mathematics is not all a priori as some people may think.

A careful study of the foregoing will be repaid with a deeper understanding of our number system, the axioms (or properties) pertaining to it, and a glimpse into the way mathematicians think. We hope it will be profitable to you in many ways in your teaching.

Division is the inverse of multiplication so that nothing new need to be learned. For example,

$$18 \div (^-6) = ^-3 \text{ because } (^-3) \times (^-6) = 18,$$
$$^-18 \div 6 = ^-3 \text{ because } (^-3) \times 6 = ^-18, \text{ and}$$
$$^-18 \div ^-6 = 3 \text{ because } 3 \times (^-6) = ^-18.$$

At the elementary level we recommend an intuitive approach to arithmetic using negative numbers. Most questions can be settled by means of the number line which now has the following appearance:

Using this line we can compare numbers, for example. We have

$$^-3 < 2,$$

since the relation " $<$ " can be read "is to the left of." We also have

$$^-3 > ^-4,$$

since the relation " $>$ " can be read "is to the right of."

Finally, we can now show that $0 \times 0 = 0$. Recall that this was postponed until now from Section 2 of Chapter 6.

Let $a$ be a rational number and consider

$$(a \times a) + (a \times 0).$$

By the distributive property,

$$(a \times a) + (a \times 0) = a \times (a + 0)$$
$$= a \times a,$$

since 0 is the additive identity

$$= (a \times a) + 0,$$

for the same reason. But

$$(a \times a) + (a \times 0) = (a \times a) + 0 \qquad (10.1)$$

implies that

$$a \times 0 = 0$$

because we can add to both members of Eq. (10.1) the additive inverse of $a \times a$.


## 2. Irrational numbers fill the gaps

All of the sets of numbers discussed so far ($N$, $W$, and $R$) have the property that their elements can be *ordered*. This means that given any two numbers $a$ and $b$ from any of these sets, precisely one of the three conditions holds,

$$a = b, a > b, a < b.$$

Furthermore, we can determine which of the three conditions holds for any two numbers $a$ and $b$.

The set $R$, however, has a property that the sets $N$ and $W$ do not have. Between any two rational numbers—no matter how nearly equal they are—one can always find another rational number. For example, $251\!/\!253$ and $252\!/\!253$ are two rational numbers whose difference is quite small, yet $503\!/\!506$ has the property

$$\frac{251}{253} < \frac{503}{506} < \frac{252}{253}.$$

In other words, $^{503}\!\!/_{506}$ is between $^{251}\!\!/_{253}$ and $^{252}\!\!/_{253}$. This process of finding other rational numbers between any two given ones can be continued *indefinitely*.

Looking at a number line, it *seems* that the line is solidly covered with rational numbers. Closer inspection, however, reveals an infinite number of gaps. We next extend our number system to fill these gaps.

We examine in detail one of the gaps on the rational number line. This gap is denoted by $\sqrt{2}$ which means *that* number which when multiplied by itself will produce 2. If you think that the rational number 1.414 (rational because it can be written as 1414/1000) is the one that answers this question, we call attention to the fact that $1.414 \times 1.414 = 1.999396 \neq 2$. Try as we might, we can never find the precise decimal representation of a number which, when multiplied by itself, will yield 2. This is due to the fact that the number $\sqrt{2}$ is a non-ending decimal. Of course, so also are

$$\tfrac{1}{3} = .3333\ldots$$
$$\tfrac{2}{7} = .285714285714\ldots$$

In every case, however, the non-ending decimal that represents a *rational* number contains a numeral or group of numerals that repeats. The number $\sqrt{2}$ is not in this category.

We call $\sqrt{2}$ an **irrational** (meaning *not* rational) number. A classical proof, originally due to Euclid, will now be given to show that $\sqrt{2}$ is not rational. The details of the proof will be carefully given so that the reader can follow each step. It is important to understand the *method* of proof that is used since this will give an insight into the manner in which a mathematician must think.

**Theorem.** $\sqrt{2}$ is not a rational number.

*Proof.*

1. *If* it were rational, we could write $\sqrt{2} = a/b$ where $a \in W$ and $b \in N$ *and* $a/b$ is in lowest terms.

2. Then multiplying both equal numbers by $\sqrt{2}$, we get

$$2 = \frac{a^2}{b^2}.$$

3. Multiplying both equal numbers by $b^2$,

$$2b^2 = a^2.$$

4. Since one of the numbers $(2b^2)$ is an even number, the other $(a^2)$ must be also.

5. If $a^2$ is even, so is $a$, since

$$\text{even} \times \text{even} = \text{even}$$
$$\text{odd} \times \text{odd} = \text{odd}.$$

6. If $a$ is even, it can be written

$$a = 2m \text{ or } a^2 = 4m^2.$$

7. Substituting this value for $a^2$ in the expression of step 3 gives

$$2b^2 = 4m^2.$$

8. Dividing both equal numbers by 2,

$$b^2 = 2m^2.$$

9. Since one of the numbers $(2m^2)$ is an even number, the other $(b^2)$ must be also.

10. If $b^2$ is even, so is $b$ as in step 5.

11. According to steps 5 and 10 it turns out that *both* $a$ and $b$ are even. But this contradicts what was said in step 1, namely, that $\sqrt{2}$ can be written as $a/b$ in *lowest* terms. In other words $\sqrt{2}$ *cannot* be written as $a/b$ in lowest terms. But this is another way of saying that $\sqrt{2}$ is not a rational number. This completes the proof of the theorem.

A more modern proof has been given by Maier and Niven.[2] Suppose that $\sqrt{2}$ is rational, say

$$\sqrt{2} = \frac{a}{b} \tag{10.2}$$

where $a$ and $b$ are natural numbers. Now, of course, every rational number has many forms. For example,

$$\tfrac{1}{2}, \tfrac{3}{6}, \tfrac{4}{8}, \tfrac{12}{24}, \tfrac{75}{150}$$

[2] Maier, E. A. and Ivan Niven: "A Method of Establishing Certain Irrationalities," *Mathematics Magazine* (37), no. 4, September 1964, p. 208.

are all equivalent—they all represent the rational number ½. In Eq. (10.2) let us consider that representation of $\sqrt{2}$ for which $b$ is the *smallest* natural number.

At this point all the additional information we have about $\sqrt{2}$ is that it lies somewhere between 1 and 2. (Why?) In other words,

$$1 < \frac{a}{b} < 2.$$

But this is the same as saying

$$b < a < 2b \text{ or}$$
$$0 < a - b < b.$$

From Eq. (10.2) we have

$$a^2 = 2b^2$$

as in Euclid's proof. Subtracting $ab$ from both of these equal quantities,

$$a^2 - ab = 2b^2 - ab.$$

Using the distributive property,

$$a \times (a - b) = b \times (2b - a).$$

Finally, dividing both of these equal quantities by $b \times (a - b)$,

$$\frac{a}{b} = \frac{2b - a}{a - b}. \tag{10.3}$$

It is important to realize that $a \neq b$ (why?), hence $a - b \neq 0$, otherwise the last division would be meaningless.

Now we are ready to finish the argument. We tried to express $\sqrt{2}$ as $a/b$ with the smallest possible value of $b$. It turns out, however, that by Eq. (10.3),

$$\sqrt{2} = \frac{a}{b} = \frac{2b - a}{a - b}.$$

In other words, $\sqrt{2}$ has now been expressed as a rational number with a denominator *smaller* than $b$. Moreover, because of the relation $b < a$, $a - b$ is also a natural number.

Thus we have reached a contradiction by correct logical reasoning.

This can happen only if we start with a *false* assumption. Our assumption was that $\sqrt{2} = a/b$ with $a$ and $b$ natural numbers. The conclusion is that $\sqrt{2}$ *cannot* be expressed in this way, that is, $\sqrt{2}$ is *not* a rational number.

We have proved the existence of *one* irrational number. By a simple extension of these ideas it turns out that the following numbers,

$$\frac{\sqrt{2}}{2}, \frac{\sqrt{2}}{3}, \frac{\sqrt{2}}{4}, \frac{\sqrt{2}}{5}, \frac{\sqrt{2}}{6}, \ldots, 2\sqrt{2}, 3\sqrt{2}, 4\sqrt{2}, \ldots$$

are also irrational. Hence from a single irrational number we can obtain whole infinities of other irrational numbers. All of these may be used to fill the gaps in the rational number line. Some other irrational numbers are $\sqrt{3}$, $\sqrt{5}$, $\sqrt{7}$, $\sqrt[3]{2}$ (the number which when multiplied by itself twice will give 2), and $\pi$ (the ratio of the circumference of a circle to its diameter).

The irrational numbers and the rational numbers are elements of the set we call the **set of real numbers**. This set $Re$ contains all the elements of the sets previously discussed. Thus

$$N \subset W \subset R \subset Re.$$

The real numbers have the same properties **A1-A5, M1-M5,** and **D** listed for the rational numbers.

The reader might well wonder how much more our number system can be extended beyond the real numbers. It turns out that, just as we extended the set of natural numbers $N$ to the set of whole numbers $W$ by adding a single number (zero) to $N$, we can do a similar thing to $Re$. By adding a single number to $Re$ we obtain the set $C$ of *complex numbers*. This set then fits into the chain as follows:

$$N \subset W \subset R \subset Re \subset C,$$

and this is as far as we can go. The set $C$ is usually first studied in high school.

## Exercises 10C

1. Evaluate (using the number line): (a) $^{-}3 + 2$   (b) $(^{-}2) + (^{-}3)$   (c) $3 + (^{-}4)$   (d) $1 - (^{-}3)$   (e) $(^{-}3) - (^{-}2)$.

2. Evaluate: (a) $7 \times (^-3)$  (b) $11 \div (^-4)$  (c) $\frac{3}{4} \times (^-\frac{2}{3})$
   (d) $(^-15) \div (^-5)$.

3. What is the additive inverse of $\frac{9}{8}$; of $(^-5)$; of zero?

4. Give two rational numbers between $^{251}\!\!/_{253}$ and $^{503}\!\!/_{506}$.

5. Modify Euclid's proof to prove that $\sqrt{3}$ is an irrational number.

6. Which of the following numbers are irrational: 1.414, 1.732, $\sqrt{5}$, 3.1416?

7. Draw a Venn diagram showing the relation between the sets $N$, $W$, $R$, and $Re$.

8. What is the additive inverse of the multiplicative inverse of $\frac{2}{3}$?

9. Place the proper sign ($>$, $<$, $=$) between the following pairs of numbers: (a) $^-6$, $^-7$  (b) $3$, $^-\frac{1}{3}$  (c) $\sqrt{3}$, 1.732  (d) 0.333, $\frac{1}{3}$.

10. Explain why $(\frac{1}{3}) \times \sqrt{2}$ is an irrational number.

# 11/Geometry (C)

## 1. Polyhedra and Euler's law

The simplest figures in space are *surfaces*. Of these, the best known is the sphere. A **sphere** is a surface or a *set of points* in space such that every point of the set is a constant distance from a fixed point. The fixed point is called the **center** of the sphere, the constant distance its *radius*.

Like all other geometric configurations we have studied, a sphere is invisible since it is really a set of points. Note carefully that according to our definition a bowling ball is *not* a sphere. A sphere is a surface, so that a layer of dust on the ball would come closer to describing a surface.

If we wish to describe an object like a bowling ball, we may refer to it as a *solid* sphere or a spherical solid. The distinction is similar to that between a circle and a circular disc, or that between a triangle and a triangular region.

One of the most interesting class of surfaces that can be studied in the elementary school is the class consisting of various *polyhedra*. We shall begin by describing the simplest polyhedron.

Suppose we have a triangle and a point not in the plane of the triangle. The three line segments forming the sides of the triangle are sets of points and each is an infinite set. The point not in the plane of the triangle is another point so that altogether we have "quite a few" points to start with.

Next, suppose we consider all possible line segments that are determined by any pairs of points. It should be clear that joining all possible pairs of points in the original triangle will give us a triangular region. If we now join *each* point of the triangular region with the point not in the plane of the triangle, we will have a space figure called a **solid tetrahedron.** Such an object is shown in Figure 11.1. Here

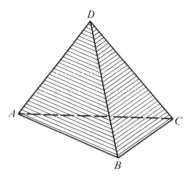

**Figure 11.1**

the original triangle has vertices $A$, $B$, and $C$ and the point not in the plane of the triangle is designated as $D$.

This figure is called a *tetra*hedron because it has *four* faces. These faces are the triangular regions $ABC$, $ABD$, $BCD$, and $ACD$. The four points $A$, $B$, $C$, and $D$ are called the **vertices** of the tetrahedron. The six line segments $AB$, $BC$, $CA$, $AD$, $BD$, and $CD$ are the **edges** of the tetrahedron.

The union of the four triangular regions is a surface called a tetrahedron. If the points *inside* the tetrahedron are also joined to the tetrahedron, we obtain a solid tetrahedron. It should be stressed that the figure the pupils make out of cardboard or construction paper is properly called a tetrahedron.

Instead of starting with a triangle, we could have started with a quadrilateral. This would have led to a pentahedron and a solid pentahedron. Starting with a pentagon would have led to a hexahedron and a solid hexahedron. In general, if we begin with a polygon and a point not in the plane of the polygon, we obtain a polyhedron or a solid polyhedron.

We observe that in the case of the tetrahedron it turns out that

$$F + V - E = 2$$

where $F$ represents the number of faces, $V$ the number of vertices, and $E$ the number of edges. The relationship between these quantities can be verified for other polyhedra. It was Euler[1] who discovered this fact in 1752 and it has since been known as "Euler's Law."

## 2. Constructions

In the course of the work in geometry we must do a number of simple constructions. These can all be done with compass and straightedge.[2] The simplest construction is to duplicate a line segment. This means that given a line segment of a certain length, such as $AB$, the student

should be able to duplicate this on the line $\overset{\leftrightarrow}{CD}$. By setting the point of the compass on point $A$ and striking an arc through $B$, the compass

is properly set. Putting the compass point on the line $\overset{\leftrightarrow}{CD}$ and striking an arc will then duplicate segment $AB$ on line $\overset{\leftrightarrow}{CD}$.

A natural extension of this idea is to duplicate a given triangle. Here it is also necessary to use a protractor in order to duplicate the angles. The details are left to the reader. Later, angles will be duplicated *without* a protractor.

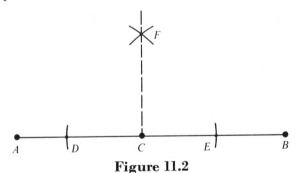

**Figure 11.2**

[1] Leonhard Euler (1707–1783), a Swiss mathematician, was one of the great mathematicians of all time. His work had an influence on almost every branch of mathematics. He is considered to be the most prolific mathematician who ever lived. This is even more remarkable when one considers that at the age of 61 he became totally blind but continued to do outstanding work.

[2] The distinction between "ruler" and "straightedge" is that the latter has no markings of any kind.

One of the most useful geometrical constructions consists of drawing a line segment perpendicular to a given line segment. Suppose we have $AB$ and wish to draw a perpendicular to $AB$ through the point $C$ (Figure 11.2). The procedure is to set the compass point at $C$ and strike off equal (but arbitrary) arcs at $D$ and $E$. Then open the compass slightly and using $D$ as center strike an arc (through $F$); also using $E$ as center strike a second arc (through $F$). The point $F$ where these two arcs intersect determines $FC$, the required line segment perpendicular to $AB$ through point $C$.

Another construction consists of drawing a line parallel to a given line segment through a point not on the given line segment. Referring to Figure 11.3 we have $LM$ and a point $N$ not on $LM$. We wish to draw

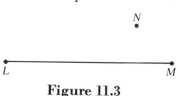

Figure 11.3

a line through $N$ which will be parallel to $LM$. There are a number of ways of accomplishing this.

One way is to draw any line (see Fig. 11.4), such as $\overleftrightarrow{NP}$ through $N$ and intersecting $LM$ at $R$. Using a protractor, measure $\angle LRN$ and duplicate this angle at $SNT$. The line $\overleftrightarrow{SN}$ will then have the required properties.

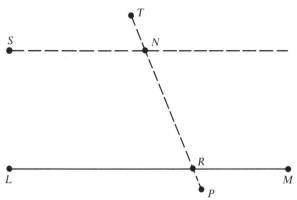

Figure 11.4

Next, we can *bisect* a line segment or an angle (Figure 11.5). To bisect $AB$ we use $A$ as center and strike a convenient arc, then use $B$

Chapter 11

as center and strike another arc intersecting the first one at $C$. Then repeat the procedure to obtain $D$. The line $\overleftrightarrow{CD}$ will meet $AB$ at $E$ which will be the mid-point of $AB$. All four arcs may be the *same* in this construction.

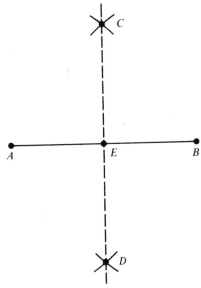

**Figure 11.5**

To bisect the angle $FGH$ (see Fig. 11.6) we use $G$ as center and strike equal arcs intersecting $\overline{GF}$ and $\overline{GH}$ in $K$ and $L$ respectively. With $K$ and $L$ as centers we then strike equal arcs intersecting at $M$. Thus $\overrightarrow{GM}$ bisects $\angle FGH$.

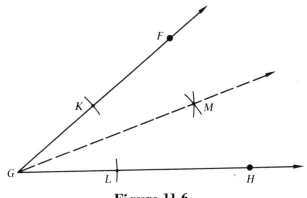

**Figure 11.6**

In a very similar manner we can duplicate an angle. Given $\angle FGH$ (Figure 11.7) we can duplicate this angle, say with segment $CD$ as one of the sides. Setting the compass point on $G$, we strike arcs inter-

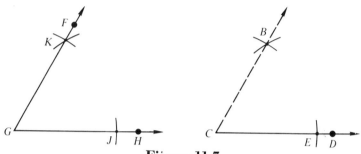

**Figure 11.7**

secting $\overrightarrow{GH}$ at $J$, $\overrightarrow{GF}$ at $K$ and $CD$ at $E$. Setting the compass point on $J$ we adjust the compass opening so that it is the length of segment $JK$. Transferring the compass to $E$, we intersect the previously drawn arc at $B$. The ray $\overrightarrow{CB}$ then completes $\angle BCD$ which is a duplicate of $\angle FGH$.

These geometrical constructions are useful not only because they give the student a preview of the geometry that is to come but also because they provide a welcome change of pace in the study of arithmetic. The latter is appreciated by both student and teacher. Variety is one of the characteristics of the new mathematics and it is a good way to keep interest at a peak and promote learning.

### 3. Congruence and similarity

It has been common practice in arithmetic to write such nonsense as $\sqrt{2} = 1.414$.[3] This is a careless use of the "equals" symbol. In geometry, however, we have been even more careless.

Consider the following "classical" proof.

**Theorem.** Given the isosceles triangle $ABC$ having equal sides $AB$ and $BC$, then the median[4] to side $AC$ divides the triangle into two congruent triangles.

---

[3] Note that $(1.414)^2 = 1.999396$ which is less than 2, hence it would be correct to say $1.414 < \sqrt{2}$.

[4] The median to a side is the line segment from the opposite vertex to the mid-point of the side.

156                                                                 **Chapter 11**

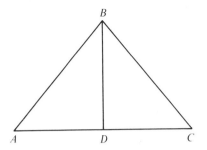

| Statement | Reason |
|---|---|
| 1. $AB = BC$ | 1. Given |
| 2. $AD = DC$ | 2. $BD$ is the median to side $AC$ |
| 3. $BD = BD$ | 3. Obvious |
| 4. ∴ $\triangle ABD \cong \triangle DBC$ | 4. sss = sss |

What is wrong with the above? Only statements 3 and 4 are correct. Statement 1 is incorrect because a line segment is actually a set—a set of points. But two sets are equal only if they contain the same elements. Since $AB$ and $BC$ have only one element in common (the point $B$), they cannot possibly be equal. Similarly, $AD$ and $DC$ have only the point $D$ in common, hence they cannot be equal.

We can compare (or relate) the measures of two line segments as

$$m(AB) = m(BC)$$

or their lengths as

$$\text{length } (AB) = \text{length } (BC).$$

What we need here, however, is the concept of *congruence of line segments*. If we place a point of a compass on point $B$ and open the compass so that the other end coincides with $A$, then we have made, in effect, a representation of $AB$ and we can move this representation about. Keeping one end of the compass on $B$, we can swing the other end from $A$ to $BC$ where the compass arc will pass through $C$. When this happens we say that $AB$ **is congruent to** $BC$ (written: $AB \cong BC$). In like manner we have $AD \cong DC$.

We call attention to the fact that it is correct to say $\overrightarrow{AD} = \overrightarrow{AC}$ and $\overrightarrow{AD} = \overrightarrow{DC}$. The first is correct because $\overrightarrow{AD}$ and $\overrightarrow{AC}$ are two different ways to designate the same ray, that is, the one having an end-point at $A$ and containing the points $C$ and $D$. The second is correct because

*A, D,* and *C* are points on the same line and it is immaterial which two points of a line are used to designate that line.

It is quite natural to extend the above ideas to congruence of angles, triangles, and polygons in general. In fact, we say that two circles are congruent if they have congruent radii.

Another important concept in geometry is that of *similarity*. Looking at Figure 11.8, it is obvious that $\triangle ABC$ is not congruent to $\triangle A'B'C'$.

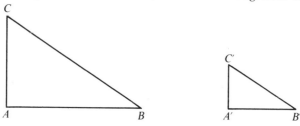

**Figure 11.8**

Still there is *some* relationship between the two triangles. They are both right triangles whose corresponding angles are congruent, that is,

$$\angle ACB \cong \angle A'C'B' \text{ and } \angle ABC \cong A'B'C'.$$

Moreover, measurement indicates that the measure of $AC$ is twice that of $A'C'$; the measure of $AB$ is twice that of $A'B'$; the measure of $BC$ is twice that of $C'B'$. In other words, the *ratio* of the measures of the sides of $\triangle ABC$ to the measures of the corresponding sides of $\triangle A'B'C'$ is a constant—in this case two. Under these conditions the two triangles are said to be **similar** to each other and we write $\triangle ABC \sim \triangle A'B'C'$. The constant ratio between the lengths (or measures) of similar figures may be an integer like 2, 3, 5, 1000, or even 1; it may be a rational number like $\frac{1}{2}$, $\frac{3}{4}$, $3\frac{1}{2}$; or it may be irrational like $\sqrt{2}$ or $\sqrt{3}$.

As a result of our description of similar figures it follows that there is also a relationship between corresponding *areas* of similar figures.

It is the concept of similarity that is used in making maps, architect's drawings, blueprints, photographic enlargements, or in movie projection or designing optical instruments.

## 4. Graphing

One of the features of the new approach to mathematics teaching is one that we might call *unification*. In the past arithmetic, geometry and algebra were taught in separate courses, while today we teach topics from them at every level. True that arithmetic still occupies the major portion of the work in mathematics at the elementary level, but there are other topics which provide welcome variety. One of them is geometry which we have already discussed. Another topic is that of *applications*.

We believe that stressing computational skill alone can make mathematics a boring subject to learn and to teach. By introducing material which uses the skills when they are learned, we are relieving the monotony and actually strengthening the skills. It is part of the new attitude toward drill.

One of the applications which can come quite early is making graphs. A graph is a means of making a pictorial representation in mathematics. It can be simple or quite abstract and thus graphs can be made at various grade levels. In order to make a graph a student must understand scaling, estimating, rounding and he must have imagination. Since there are a number of places where these traits are important, making graphs has many educational advantages.

The simplest graph is one that shows how many fish each of four fishermen caught during the week or one that shows how many children are enrolled in several elementary schools. As soon as we start talking about larger numbers such as 35 fish or 728 students, it is necessary to use some kind of *scale*. We may decide, for example, to draw a picture of a fish and let that picture represent 10 fish. To this scale 35 fish would be represented by pictures of three fish and one-half of a fish. In the second case we could have a picture of a student representing 100 students and we would then need seven such pictures and about ¼ of a picture. The advantage of this kind of graph (called a picture graph) is that it does not require any great artistic ability. In fact, students who have no artistic ability can cut pictures out of discarded magazines and use them or tracings of them.

It is now just a step to go from the picture to the *bar graph* in which the height of the bar represents a certain number. Notice how naturally this leads into a study of *ratios*—if a bar one inch high represents $20, then a bar 2½ inches high will represent $50 because $1/20 = 2½/50$. (The properties of the number system again!)

The next step is the *circle graph* which again uses the idea of ratio but also uses angle measure and rational numbers between zero and one. Actually, the circle graph can be introduced quite early because it can be used to show what happens to a weekly allowance, assuming it is spent on no more than, say, four items. By encouraging estimation, a satisfactory circle graph can be made by children before they know anything about angle measure or fractions.

By the sixth grade we are ready to make *broken-line graphs* based on the amount of rainfall (in inches) per month or on the number of persons killed in traffic accidents per week.

The final step in graphing can be reached by introducing a *coordinate system*. This may be done effectively by considering a city that has *streets* running east and west and *avenues* running north and south. Intersections can then be identified by saying, for example, "third street and fifth avenue." This can then be shortened to the *pair* of numbers 3 and 5. Note that this is *not* the same as the pair 5 and 3 because this means the intersection of fifth street and third avenue. Thus we develop the important idea of an *ordered pair* such as (3, 5) or (5, 3).

We can extend this to a *coordinate graph* where we have a starting point or *origin* (say, the public square) and on which we can locate various intersections. It is but a step to draw straight lines from one intersection to another.

In this way we have taken the subject of graphing through the elementary grades and have arrived finally at the doorstep to *analytic geometry*. It is hardly possible for a teacher to guide this development unless he is familiar with all the steps along the way. In teaching mathematics a teacher must know what is going on in his class, what preceded his class, and what is yet to come. This is one of the characteristics of the new mathematics—a teacher cannot afford to be just a day ahead of his class.

## Exercises 11C

**1.** Check Euler's law for a pentahedron; for a hexahedron.

**2.** How many edges, vertices, and faces does an octahedron have?

**3.** Describe how to duplicate a given rectangle.

4. What is the most general solution to the following problem: Find all points which are equidistant from two given points?

5. Using the diameter of a semicircle as one of the sides, construct a triangle s that the third vertex is on the semicircle.

6. Repeat exercise 5 by choosing the third point at various places on the semicircle. What common characteristic do all these triangles have?

7. Draw any triangle and construct its medians. Where do these medians meet?

8. Draw any triangle and construct the bisectors of its angles. Where do these bisectors meet?

9. Are all circles similar? Explain.

10. Are all squares similar? Explain.

11. Are all rectangles similar? Explain.

12. Draw any triangle. Locate the mid-points of its sides. Draw the triangle having these points as vertices.

13. What conclusion can you draw concerning the two triangles of exercise 12?

14. If the sides of one triangle are double the length of the corresponding sides of another triangle, how are the areas of the two triangles related?

15. On a bar graph one inch represents 100 pupils. How would you represent 350 pupils? 425 pupils? 567 pupils?

16. Locate the following points on a coordinate system: (2,0), (0,2), (−2,0), (0, −2).

17. Considering the four points of exercise 16 as vertices, what kind of figure do they form?

18. What common characteristic do the following points have: (−3,4), (3,4), (−3, −4), (5,0)?

# 12/Number Theory (G)

## 1. Ordering of the real numbers

We have seen that the real numbers completely cover the number line. To every point on the line there corresponds a real number and, conversely, every real number can be represented by a point. Since points have no size, this correspondence between points and numbers exists only in the imagination. We cannot, for example, show pictorially the distinct points corresponding to 1.4598 and 1.4597 unless we magnify the scale on our number line.

It is a fact, however, that given any two different real numbers we can ascertain which is the larger. Another way of saying this is that we can tell which of two real numbers is "to the right of" the other on the number line.

Thus we say that the real numbers can be *ordered*—we can start with a bushel basket of real numbers and sort them out according to magnitude. This idea should be stressed in the elementary school because otherwise pupils may have difficulty in differentiating between numbers.

There is usually no trouble encountered when we examine number pairs like the following:

| | |
|------|------|
| 269  | 273  |
| 299  | 301  |
| 1909 | 1910 |
| 5599 | 5600 |

In each case the smaller of the two number pairs is in the left column.

Decimal numbers are more difficult to compare unless we remember the place values of the various digits. For example, consider the following list:

| | |
|---|---|
| 3.289 | 3.301 |
| 2.909 | 2.910 |
| 6.01759 | 6.02 |

Again the smaller number in each pair is in the left column. The criterion for comparison remains the same: as we examine each digit from left to right we note the first place value where the digits differ and base our conclusion on this. In comparing 6.01759 and 6.02, we note that these numbers have the same digit in the ones place and in the tenths place. In the hundredths place, however, one number has the digit 1 while the other has the digit 2. Hence 6.01759 is less than 6.02. We need look no further!

We can thus answer questions regarding which of two numbers is the greater. Or can we? What about 2.9999 . . . and 3? At first glance we would have a tendency to say $3 > 2.9999 \ldots$ . The number 2.9999 . . . is an infinite repeating decimal and all such numbers are rational numbers. The question is: which rational number corresponds to 2.9999 . . . ?

Let $N$ be the rational number that corresponds to $2.9999 \ldots$ . In other words,

$$N = 2.9999 \ldots$$

Then

$$10N = 29.999 \ldots \quad .$$

If now we subtract $N$ from 10 N, we get

$$9N = 27.0000 \ldots \quad . \qquad \text{(Why?)}$$

From this it follows that $N = 3$. Hence

$$2.9999 \ldots = 3 \quad .$$

The above case represents the only real difficulty we meet in ordering the real numbers—at least on the elementary level. All other problems are solved by considering *place value*.


## 2. Relations

We have almost lost sight of the fact that mathematics is a game—an honest game. There has been much to learn and many of the ideas were quite abstract so that we were hard put to it sometimes to tie them together with reality. The fact remains though that many of the things we have discussed have their analogies in a game.

At one time we played the game of natural numbers according to certain fixed and inviolable rules. We also had certain *relations* between the pieces in this game. For example,

$$5 < 7$$
$$5 + 2 = 7$$
$$5 + 3 = 8 > 7.$$

In geometry we had certain relations between line segments. For example, $AB$ might be perpendicular to $CD$ and parallel to $EF$.

In studying sets we found that set $A$ could be equal to set $B$, a subset of set $C$, and equivalent to set $D$. These are *relations* between sets.

While all these relations between mathematical entities are important, there is one which merits special mention. This is the *equivalence relation*, that is, the relation that expresses that two things are in some way equivalent. Note that the word "equivalent" is *not* to be interpreted here as "identical to." True, the latter is one form of an equivalence relation but a rather special one.

What do we mean when we write

$$8 = VIII?$$

Surely, the arabic numeral 8 is not identical to the Roman numeral VIII. We mean, rather, that 8 and VIII express the same idea, that they are equivalent. The symbols $5 + 3$ and 8 are to be similarly interpreted.

An equivalence relation is characterized by three properties. Let $A$, $B$ and $C$ be numbers, line segments, sets, or what have you, and $R$ be a relation ($<$, $>$, $=$, $\perp$, $\parallel$, $\approx$, etc.). Then $R$ is an equivalence relation if the following three properties are satisfied:

1. $A\ R\ A$ (Reflexive).
2. If $A\ R\ B$, then $B\ R\ A$ (Symmetric).
3. If $A\ R\ B$ and $B\ R\ C$, then $A\ R\ C$ (Transitive).

Ordinary equality ($=$) is an equivalence relation because

1. $a = a$, for any $a$ whatever.

2. If $a = b$, then $b = a$.
3. If $a = b$ and $b = c$, then $a = c$.

For example, using rational numbers,

1. $\frac{3}{4} = \frac{3}{4}$.
2. If $\frac{3}{4} = \frac{6}{8}$, then $\frac{6}{8} = \frac{3}{4}$.
3. If $\frac{3}{4} = \frac{6}{8}$ and $\frac{6}{8} = \frac{12}{16}$, then $\frac{3}{4} = \frac{12}{16}$.

Equivalence of sets ($\approx$) is an equivalence relation because

1. $A \approx A$ for any set $A$.
2. If $A \approx B$, then $B \approx A$ since a one-to-one correspondence is symmetric.
3. If $A \approx B$ and $B \approx C$, then $A \approx C$ which follows from the process of matching the elements of one set with another.

The relation ($<$) is *not* an equivalence relation because

1. $a < a$ is false for every $a$.
2. If $a < b$, then $b < a$ is false.
3. If $a < b$ and $b < c$, then $a < c$ is true.

The relation ($\parallel$) (read: is parallel to) is an equivalence relation because

1. $AB \parallel AB$ for any line segment $AB$.
2. If $AB \parallel DC$, then $CD \parallel AB$.
3. If $AB \parallel CD$ and $CD \parallel EF$, then $AB \parallel EF$ in an obvious way.

The relation ($\perp$) (read: is perpendicular to) is *not* an equivalence relation because

1. $AB \perp AB$ is false.
2. If $AB \perp CD$, then $CD \perp AB$ is true.
3. If $AB \perp CD$ and $CD \perp EF$, then $AB \perp EF$ is false—the correct conclusion is $AB \parallel EF$.

The relation $\subseteq$ (is a subset of) is *not* an equivalence relation because

1. $A \subseteq A$ is true for any set $A$.
2. If $A \subseteq B$, then $B \subseteq A$ is false (Why?)
3. If $A \subseteq B$ and $B \subseteq C$, then $A \subseteq C$ is true.

Since we defined an equivalence relation as one that satisfied *three* conditions, a relation that does not satisfy *one* of these conditions cannot be an equivalence relation.

Equivalence relations are also found in non-mathematical situations. The relation "is a relative of" which we can shorten to *iaro* for convenience is an equivalence relation when applied to people because

1. *A* iaro *A* for any person *A* (we remark that this is a rather close relationship even though it does not have any special name).
2. If *A* iaro *B*, then *B* iaro *A* is true.
3. If *A* iaro *B* and *B* iaro *C*, then *A* iaro *C* is true.

It is important to note that when we talk about relations we must also specify the set from which come the elements to which the relation can be applied. The relation can have no meaning without knowing the set. For instance, in our examples of the relations $\parallel$ and $\perp$ it is especially important to state that the line segments which are being related (or compared) are all in the same plane.

## 3. The duodecimal system of numeration—base 12

At the sixth grade level students reach a mathematical maturity so that they are capable of understanding the duodecimal system (base 12). The reason this system requires more maturity for understanding is that in the duodecimal system we have *twelve* digits and place values are powers of twelve. The first 10 of these digits are, quite naturally,

$$0, 1, 2, 3, 4, 5, 6, 7, 8, 9.$$

We cannot, however, write 10 for the next numeral because in this system 10 represents twelve—that is *one* twelve plus *zero* ones. Similarly 11 represents thirteen and not eleven as we would like.

Our difficulty here is that we have only *ten* digits and must invent other symbols for systems of numeration higher than 10. In the duodecimal system, for example, we could count,

$$\ldots 8, 9, \$, \#$$

or

$$\ldots 8, 9, \varsigma, \alpha$$

or in some similar fashion. The main thing to keep in mind is that the two additional new digits must have a value of *ten* and *eleven*. Thus, instead of having to learn *new* symbols, it is easier to count,

$$\ldots 8, 9, T, E$$

and use the symbols "T" and "E" to represent ten and eleven.

A typical numeral in the duodecimal system would have the following appearance: 9T4E. This means,

$$(9 \times 12^3) + (10 \times 12^2) + (4 \times 12) + (11 \times 1)$$

or

$$(9 \times 1728) + (10 \times 144) + (4 \times 12) + (11 \times 1)$$

or

$$15\,552 + 1\,440 + 48 + 11$$

which is 17 051 in the decimal system. Hence

$$(9T4E)_{12} = (17\,051)_{10}.$$

Conversely,

$$
\begin{array}{r|r c}
12 & 17051 & \\
12 & 1420 & 11 \\
12 & 118 & 4 \\
& 9 & 10 \\
\end{array}
$$

This means that 11 (or E) goes in the 1's place, 4 in the 12's place, 10 (or T) in the 144's place and 9 in the 1728's place.

We will not attempt to do any arithmetic in the duodecimal system but we will convert several numerals from one system to the other.

$$
\begin{aligned}
(T0E)_{12} &= (10 \times 144) + (0 \times 12) + (11 \times 1) \\
&= 1440 + 0 + 11 \\
&= (1451)_{10}
\end{aligned}
$$

$$
\begin{aligned}
(4916)_{12} &= (4 \times 12^3) + (9 \times 12^2) + (1 \times 12) + (6 \times 1) \\
&= (4 \times 1728) + (9 \times 144) + (1 \times 12) + (6 \times 1) \\
&= 6912 + 1296 + 12 + 6 \\
&= (8226)_{10}.
\end{aligned}
$$

By inspection,

$$(56)_{10} = 48 + 8$$
$$= (4 \times 12) + (8 \times 1)$$
$$= (48)_{12}$$

$$(443)_{10} = 432 + 11$$
$$= (3 \times 144) + (11 \times 1)$$
$$= (3 \times 144) + (0 \times 12) + (11 \times 1)$$
$$= (30E)_{12}.$$

Note that in this last example it was *essential* to indicate a zero in the 12's place. This is consistent with our procedure in the decimal system or in *any* place-value system of numeration.

## 4. Number and numeral

So far we have deliberately not stressed the distinction between *number* and *numeral*. We believe that this distinction is more easily understood and better appreciated *after* the student has acquired an understanding of the ideas in the foregoing chapters.

Consider the idea conveyed by the word "three." What does this really mean? The word is not defined in a dictionary although it brings to mind many different things. Some of these are the following:

> trio
> triumvirate
> trinity
> eternal triangle
> a crowd
> tricolor
> triple
> triplets.

Which one you prefer depends on whether you lean toward music, religion, patriotism, baseball, or sex. In other words, the word "three" has many connotations.

When we study mathematics, however, we are interested in the *mathematical* significance of the word "three." We define it as "one more than two" and we define two as "one more than one." The idea of "one" we accept and do not try to define.

Everyone has an intuitive feeling about what "three" means in mathematics. Yet the *number* exists only in the mind. We can give *examples* of it but the idea is an abstract one.

On the other hand, there are many *numerals* which represent the number three. Following are some numerals that represent three:

$$2 + 1$$
$$5 - 2$$
$$12 \div 4$$
$$1 \times 3$$
$$3 + 0$$
$$3$$
$$\text{III}$$
$$\sqrt{9}$$
$$(11)_2$$
$$\text{drei}$$
$$\text{trois}$$
$$\text{három.}$$

In other words, a numeral is a *symbol* or a *name* for a number. In the above list the last three names are names for the number three in German, French, and Hungarian, respectively.

The whole point of all this is that *every* number has many names. What we said about three in the preceding discussion could apply equally well to ten, eight, one, zero, one-half, or other numbers.

The rational number one-half also has many names. Some of these are the following:

$$0.5$$
$$50\%$$
$$\tfrac{3}{6}$$
$$\tfrac{39}{78}$$
$$6 \div 12$$
$$^-3 + 3\tfrac{1}{2}$$
$$(0.4)_8$$
$$(1/\sqrt{2})^2.$$

Thus, a number is an abstract idea and a numeral is a symbol or a name used to represent the idea. This distinction should be taught as early as possible, but you should keep in mind that the second grade is *not* the place to say, "What do you mean, Johnny, the number three or the numeral that represents three?"

## Exercises 12C

1. Which of the following two numbers is the larger: $1\frac{9}{9}$, 1.111? Why?

2. Which of the following two numbers is the larger: $\sqrt{2}$, $\sqrt[3]{3}$?[1] Why?

3. What rational number is represented by 2.878787 . . . ? (Hint: Use the method of Section 1, that is, let $N = 2.878787$ . . . and express $100N$; then subtract, etc.).

4. Prove that the relation $\sim$ (is similar to) is an equivalence relation.

5. Is the relation $\leq$ an equivalence relation? Why?

6. Write the number "eight" as follows:
   (a) Using addition
   (b) Using subtraction
   (c) Using multiplication
   (d) Using division
   (e) Using exponent notation
   (f) Using Roman numerals
   (g) Using a foreign language
   (h) Using square root notation
   (i) Using percent
   (j) Using the distributive law
   (k) Using base 5
   (l) Using some other notation different from the above.

7. Examine the relation "is a contemporary of" as applied to people. Is it an equivalence relation?

8. Convert the duodecimal numeral T00 to its decimal equivalent.

9. What is $(T0E)_{12}$ in the octal system?

10. Convert the decimal numeral 6789 to its duodecimal equivalent.

11. What is the duodecimal equivalent of $(4302)_5$?

12. Convert $(110110111)_2$ to the duodecimal system.

13. What is $(T0T)_{12}$ in the quinary system? in the decimal system?

14. Under what conditions can we say that $6 + 6 = 10$?

15. Express the number zero in at least eight different ways.

---

[1] $\sqrt[3]{3}$ is that number which when multiplied by itself *twice* is three. For example, $\sqrt[3]{8}$ is 2 because $2 \times 2 \times 2 = 8$.

# 13/*Problem Solving*

## 1. Sentences and transliteration

One of the most difficult topics in elementary mathematics is that of problem solving. The phrase "word problem" or "verbal problem" or "story problem" or however it is disguised is enough to strike terror into the heart of student and teacher alike.

Now we do not claim that problem solving in the new mathematics curriculum will be simple or a routine matter. Problem solving will always be difficult because it requires thinking—it cannot be done automatically. The point is that in modern mathematics teaching we encourage thinking all along the way. Thus, when we come to problem solving we ask the students to do *more* thinking but it is not nearly so much more than they had to do before. We're going from the tenth to the fourteenth floor, rather than from the ground floor to the fourteenth floor.

At the present time we expect to have difficulty with problems but after a student has had a year or two of modern mathematics you will be surprised how he takes problems in stride. Of course, this assumes that the teacher is also growing in mathematical maturity.

Contrary to good mathematical procedure, we have been talking about problems and problem solving but have not defined anything yet. When we speak about problem solving we mean solving problems which have to be formulated by the student. This is in contrast to examples like $34 \times 27$ or $\frac{2}{3} + \frac{4}{5}$ where the problem is already formulated and the student merely has to carry out the indicated operation.

In order to formulate a problem it is necessary to write a *mathematical* sentence. Here is a wonderful opportunity for the teacher to tie

**Problem Solving** 171

mathematics in with English grammar! Following are some examples of mathematical sentences together with their English "translations":

1. $3 + 5 = 8$
   The sum of three and five is eight.
2. $4 < 7$
   Four is less than seven.
3. $3 \times 6 = 18$
   The product of three and six is eighteen.
4. $24 \div 6 = 4$
   The quotient of twenty-four and six is four.
5. $4 + 3 = 3 + 4$
   The sum of four and three is the same as the sum of three and four.
6. $\frac{2}{7} \times \frac{7}{2} = 1$
   Two-sevenths multiplied by its reciprocal is one.
7. $\sqrt{2} > 1.414$
   The square root of two is greater than one point four one four.
8. $n + 2 = 5$
   A number *increased* by two is five.
   A number is two *less* than five.
9. $n < 5$
   A number is less than five.
10. $(n \times 3) + n + 5 = 13$
    Three times a number added to five more than the number is thirteen.

Notice that in the above examples we have emphasized the similarity between the mathematical sentence and the English sentence. Both have subjects, verbs, and objects.

The first step in this work is to practice writing mathematical sentences from English sentences and vice versa. When a student is able to write a mathematical sentence from an English sentence, then he is able to *formulate* a problem.

As in grammar we begin with simple sentences like the ones shown above. These may be divided into two classes. We have **statements** (also called **propositions**) whose truth or falsity is a matter of record. Following are some examples of statements:

1. $10 - (4 + 3) = 3$

2. $6 < 2 + 5$

3. $13 \times 17 = 231$

4. $7 < 5.$

The first two are *true* statements, while the last two are *false* statements.

Non-mathematical examples of statements are the following:

1. Columbus is the capital of Ohio.

2. Beethoven and Brahms were contemporary German composers.

3. Andrew Jackson was the seventh president of the United States.

Of these, the second one is a false statement (by a few years).

In problem solving we are usually confronted with sentences which are called **open sentences.** These are statements which may be true in some cases and false in others. If this sounds paradoxical, consider the following:

1. $n$ is a divisor of 72.

2. $3 < n < 7$ and $n$ is an integer.

3. $n + 2 = 7.$

4. $x$ is a rational number.

In number 1, $n = 8$ makes a true statement out of the open sentence while $n = 5$ produces a false statement. Can you give several values for each of the *variables* ($x$ and $n$ above are called **variables**) in the four open sentences some of which produce true statements and some which produce false ones?

Some examples of non-mathematical open sentences are the following:

1. It is a river in California.

2. He was president of the United States.

3. She is an elementary teacher.

Notice that the pronouns, "it," "he," and "she" play the roles of the variables here. If in number 2 "he" refers to William Jennings Bryan, we get a false statement but if "he" refers to Thomas Jefferson, we get a true statement. Can you assign proper names to the above pronouns to obtain both true and false statements?

We have a tendency to think that the subject is the most important part of an English sentence. In mathematics, however, subject and verb have equally important status. We have to know what we are talking about as well as what the action is!

Some of the nouns or phrases we can use in a sentence are the following:

1. set
   subset
   element
   universe of discourse
   complement

   Cartesian product of sets
   cardinal number of a set
   empty set
   finite set
   infinite set
   disjoint sets

2. line
   ray
   line segment
   angle
   circle
   simple closed curve
   polygon
   triangle
   vertex
   quadrilateral
   pentagon
   hexagon

   parallelogram
   trapezoid
   plane
   half-plane
   region
   space
   tetrahedron
   sphere
   polyhedron
   edge
   face
   measure

3. counting number
   integer
   rational number
   irrational number
   real number
   additive identity
   additive inverse
   multiplicative identity
   multiplicative inverse
      (or reciprocal)
   system of numeration

   binary system
   quinary system
   octal system
   decimal system
   duodecimal system
   even number
   odd number
   prime number
   composite number
   negative number
   factor

4. operation
   binary operation
   unary operation
   inverse operation
   union of sets
   addition

   subtraction
   multiplication
   division
   square root
   exponentiation or raising
   to an exponent

5. axioms
   properties
   closure property
   commutative property
   associative property
   distributive property

   reflexive property
   symmetric property
   transitive property

Verbs which are used in mathematics include the following:

6. is equal to
   is equivalent to
   is congruent to
   is similar to
   is greater than
   is less than
   is approximately equal to

   is greater than or equal to
   is less than or equal to
   is a subset of
   is an element of
   is parallel to
   is perpendicular to
   is divisible by
   is a multiple of

7. All the negatives of the above. Most of these are straightforward but a few are tricky and merit special mention.

   $\not< $ means "is not less than," that is, "is greater than or equal to."

   $\not> $ means "is not greater than," that is, "is less than or equal to."

   $\not\leq $ means "is not less than or equal to," that is, "is greater than."

   $\not\geq $ means "is not greater than or equal to," that is, "is less than."

We next use some of the above nouns and verbs to form various mathematical sentences. We write each mathematical sentence using the standard symbols that are available and include the English translation as well.

$$n \leq 5$$

A number is at most five.

$$n \geq 8$$

A number is at least eight.

$$3 < n < 7$$

A number is between three and seven.

$$3 \leq n \leq 7$$

A number is at least three and at most seven.

$$A \approx B \Rightarrow n(A) = n(B)$$

$A$ is equivalent to $B$ implies that $A$ and $B$ have the same number of elements.

$$a \in \emptyset \text{ is a false statement}$$

The empty set cannot have any members.

$$a \in B \Rightarrow a \notin B'$$

An element that is a member of a set cannot be a member of the complement of the set.

$$a, b, c \text{ real} \Rightarrow a \times (b - c) = (a \times b) - (a \times c)$$

For real numbers multiplication is distributive over subtraction.

The ease with which one can translate from English to mathematics, and conversely, determines how much he can learn about mathematics and how successful he is in problem solving. When reading a problem we do not ask, "What shall I do—multiply or divide?" It is not possible to take action until the problem has been written in mathematical terms. Then the action will be clear because it will, in fact, be dictated by the properties of the particular system under consideration. We illustrate with some examples.

1. $\frac{2}{3}$ of a number is 8. What is the number? We write

$$\tfrac{2}{3} n = 8$$

and reason as follows: We want to know what $n$ is and this means that we must somehow "get rid of" the $\frac{2}{3}$. *If* this number were *one*, then we could say $1 \times n = n$. How can we change $\frac{2}{3}$ into 1? By multiplying $\frac{2}{3}$ by its reciprocal! If we also multiply 8 by this same reciprocal we will still be able to equate the two numbers. In other words,

$$\tfrac{2}{3} n = 8$$

can be written,

$$\tfrac{3}{4} \times \tfrac{2}{3} n = \tfrac{3}{4} \times 8.$$

This last is based on the fact that if two numbers ($\frac{4}{3}$ $n$ and 8) are equal, then if we multiply each number by $\frac{3}{4}$, the resulting products will still be equal. Now we have

$$1 \times n = 6$$

or

$$n = 6.$$

Check:

$$\frac{4}{3} \text{ of } 6 \text{ } is \text{ } 8.$$

2. Twice a number exceeds 9 by 5. What is the number? Twice a number is $2n$. For $2n$ to exceed 9 means that $2n > 9$. This inequality may be transformed into an equality if we reduce $2n$ by just the right amount so that the new number will be 9. By how much do we have to reduce $2n$ before the result is equal to 9? By 5 because $2n$ is 5 greater than 9. Thus

$$2n - 5 = 9.$$

Now $2n - 5$ and 9 are different names for the same number. Adding 5 to each of these numbers will maintain the equality. Hence

$$2n - 5 + 5 = 9 + 5$$

or

$$2n + 5 - 5 = 14$$
$$2n + 0 = 14$$
$$2n = 14,$$

using the properties of the number system. Now, just as in example 1,

$$\frac{1}{2} \times 2n = \frac{1}{2} \times 14$$
$$n = 7.$$

Check:

$$14 \text{ (twice 7) } does \text{ exceed 9 by 5.}$$

3. Find three consecutive numbers whose sum is 24. If we designate by $n$ the smallest of the three, then $n + 1$ and $n + 2$ will denote the other two. Hence

**Problem Solving**                                                    177

$$n + n + 1 + n + 2 = 24$$
$$n + n + n + 1 + 2 = 24$$
$$(1 \times n) + (1 \times n) + (1 \times n) + 3 = 24$$
$$(1 + 1 + 1) \times n + 3 = 24$$
$$(3 \times n) + 3 = 24$$
$$(3 \times n) + 3 - 3 = 24 - 3$$
$$(3 \times n) + 0 = 21$$
$$3 \times n = 21$$
$$\tfrac{1}{3} \times 3 \times n = \tfrac{1}{3} \times 21$$
$$1 \times n = 7$$
$$n = 7.$$

Note each step and the property or axiom which is used. Check: $7 + 8 + 9$ *is* 24 and 7, 8, and 9 *are* three consecutive numbers.

4. Find three consecutive odd numbers whose sum is 33. Again let us designate the smallest of the three by $n$. Then the other two will be $n + 2$ and $n + 4$. Hence

$$n + n + 2 + n + 4 = 33$$
$$n + n + n + 2 + 4 = 33$$
$$(1 \times n) + (1 \times n) + (1 \times n) + 6 = 33$$
$$(1 + 1 + 1) \times n + 6 = 33$$
$$(3 \times n) + 6 = 33$$
$$(3 \times n) + 6 - 6 = 33 - 6$$
$$(3 \times n) + 0 = 27$$
$$(3 \times n) = 27$$
$$\tfrac{1}{3} \times 3 \times n = \tfrac{1}{3} \times 27$$
$$1 \times n = 9$$
$$n = 9.$$

Check: $9 + 11 + 13$ *is* 33 and 9, 11, and 13 *are* three consecutive odd numbers.

5. There are 65 students in two sixth-grade classrooms. There are five more students in one room than in another. How many students are there in each room? It is perfectly all right to accept the answer of the student who says 30 and 35. If you press him for a reason and he can't answer anything but, "It just is," that's all right too. Some problems are obvious to some people and there is really no point in insisting on a formal solution and making the student furnish all the

horrendous details. In fact, this kind of insistence may be instrumental in turning the gifted students away from mathematics. The weaker student, on the other hand, may find some satisfaction in providing the details. If these are $n$ students in one room, there must be $n + 5$ in the other room. Thus

$$n + n + 5 = 65$$
$$(1 \times n) + (1 \times n) + 5 = 65$$
$$(1 + 1) \times n + 5 = 65$$
$$(2 \times n) + 5 = 65$$
$$(2 \times n) + 5 - 5 = 65 - 5$$
$$(2 \times n) + 0 = 60$$
$$2 \times n = 60$$
$$\tfrac{1}{2} \times 2 \times n = \tfrac{1}{2} \times 60$$
$$1 \times n = 30$$
$$n = 30$$
$$n + 5 = 35.$$

Check: 30 + 35 *is* 65 and 35 *is* 5 more than 30.

Another which can be solved with very little effort is the following: "Three times some number is 27. Find the number." Note that this statement is equivalent to "three times what number is 27?"

Sometimes a change in the wording will make the solution obvious. Try it on "one-fourth of some number is 5; find the number," and "of two numbers, one is 8 more than the other; if their sum is 34, what are the numbers?"

The following are not so obvious but you should be able to find the solutions.

a. Twice a certain number increased by 4 is 18.
b. Some number increased by 5 times itself is 36.
c. If some number is divided by 5 and the result added to 11, the total is 14.
d. What number increased by 5 is one-third of 24?
e. Three times a number less 12 is twice the number.
f. If the sum of three consecutive integers is 51, what are they?
g. Find three consecutive odd integers whose sum is 9 more than twice the next consecutive odd integer.
h. Of two numbers, one is 8 more than the other. If their sum is 34, what are the numbers?

**Problem Solving** 179

The correct reasoning and a knowledge of the properties and operations are essential to success here. But even more important is the fact that work of this kind in the elementary school may result in algebra seeming like child's play. This, in turn, may reduce the terror and the dislike and may encourage the student to go on to higher things in mathematics.

## 2. Solution sets

To "solve" a problem means to find its *solution set*. The **solution set** consists of all those values of the variable which make the given open sentence a *true* statement. For example, if the problem is to find the divisors of 72, we formulate the problem by writing the open sentence:

$$n \text{ is a divisor of 72.}$$

The solution set is the set

$$\{1,\ 2,\ 3,\ 4,\ 6,\ 8,\ 9,\ 12,\ 18,\ 36,\ 72\}.$$

That these numbers do belong in the solution set can be checked by substitution in the open sentence.

Thus we have the three basic essentials for solving problems— formulating the problem, determining the solution set, and checking the elements of the solution set. In the first introduction to problem solving, the solution set usually contains a *single* element. For example, "Find a number which is two less than seven." We would write the open sentence,

$$n + 2 = 7,$$

because if $n$ is two *less* than seven, we must *add* two before we can equate the sum to seven. By inspection (or by subtracting two from each of the equal quantities) we determine the solution set $\{5\}$. This checks because $5 + 2 = 7$. By a slightly sophisticated argument one can prove that 5 is the *only* element in the solution set. The reasoning goes as follows: Suppose there is another number in the solution set; call it $x$. Then, not only $5 + 2 = 7$, but $x + 2 = 7$ also. Why? Hence $x + 2 = 5 + 2$. Why? But when we subtract 2 from each of the equal quantities, we get $x = 5$. In other words, assuming that the solution set contains another number, we prove that this other number is 5.

To fix these ideas about solving elementary problems we give some examples. We give the problem, then the open sentence which is a formulation of the problem, then the solution set, and finally the check.

*Problem:* There are 382 children enrolled in the fourth grade of a certain school. On Monday, 27 children were absent. How many were present?

*Formulation:* $n + 27 = 382$, where $n$ represents the number present.

*Solution set:* $\{355\}$

*Check:* $355 + 27 = 382$

Note that the formulation is *not* unique! The student who writes $n = 382 - 27$ also understands the problem.

*Problem:* A man owes someone $325. He has already paid $55, $43 and $25. How much does he still owe?

*Formulation:* $55 + 43 + 25 + d = 325$, where $d$ represents the number of dollars he still owes.

*Solution set:* $\{\$202\}$

*Check:* $\$55 + \$43 + \$25 + \$202 = \$325$.
Again the formulation could have been

$$55 + 43 + 25 = 123,$$
$$d + 123 = 325,$$

or the equivalent of this. We also encourage students to write the proper units when they obtain the solution set. In the last problem the dollar sign is essential.

*Problem:* An automobile was driven 17 850 miles one year. If it used 1050 gallons of gasoline during the year, what was the average number of miles per gallon for the year?

*Formulation:* $a \times 1050 = 17\,850$, where $a$ represents the average number of miles traveled per gallon.

*Solution set:* $\{17 \text{ miles per gallon}\}$

**Problem Solving**                                                      **181**

*Check:* 17 miles per gallon $\times$ 1050 gallons = 17 850 miles. Here the solution is obtained by applying the *inverse* of multiplication. If one wants to "undo" multiplication by 1050, as in this case, it can be done by *dividing* by 1050. Notice that in checking the last problem, we carried the units along. This is done to give the student practice in working with **denominate numbers,** that is, numbers to which units are attached.

*Problem:* Paul wants to cut strips of wood each $10\frac{1}{2}$ inches long. He needs five such strips and knows he must allow $\frac{1}{8}$ inch for each saw cut. How long a board does he need in order to make 5 strips?

*Formulation:* Here it is essential to draw a figure first and label it correctly.

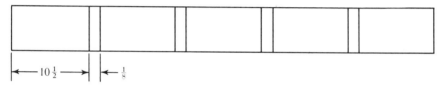

$L = (5 \times 10\frac{1}{2}) + (4 \times \frac{1}{8})$, where $L$ is the length of the board in inches.

*Solution set:* $\{53 \text{ inches}\}$

*Check:* $(5 \times 10\frac{1}{2} \text{ inches}) + (4 \times \frac{1}{8} \text{ inch}) = 53$ inches

In problem solving students should be encouraged to demonstrate their individual differences. There is no "pat" way to solve most problems, and to try to classify them by "types" becomes a hopeless task. There is just no substitute for thinking!

## 3. Dimensional analysis

In much of mathematics we are not dealing with just numbers but with numbers to which units are attached. Thus we speak of 18 *inches*, 45 *minutes*, 60 *miles per hour*, 5 *bottles*, and so on.

Students sometimes have difficulty with problems involving units (or **dimensions**) because they do not realize that the dimension is an important part of the number. Verbal problems are especially troublesome if the dimensions are neglected. For example, we find students adding 18 and 45 when these numbers are really 18 inches and 45 minutes. Adding inches to minutes is as ridiculous as adding cabbages and kings!

It will be shown that the concept of dimensionality is important not only because it reduces errors but because it makes the work easier. Attaining greater efficiency in mathematics should be one of the most important aims in mathematics teaching.

The concept of dimensionality will be illustrated by means of several examples taken from elementary textbooks.

1. How many inches in 23 feet?
   This question is more correctly stated, "How many inches are equivalent to 23 feet?" We begin with 23 feet and multiply this by *one*. However, we use a form of "one" that will produce inches. Since 12 inches is equivalent to 1 foot, the ratio 12 in./1 ft behaves in this case like one, the multiplicative identity. Thus

   $$23 \text{ ft} \times \frac{12 \text{ in.}}{1 \text{ ft}} = 276 \text{ in.}$$

   solves the problem. In other words, 23 feet is equivalent to 276 inches.

2. The school is mimeographing a school paper. Each copy of the paper uses 8 sheets. If 240 papers are run off how many reams of paper are necessary? (One ream equals 480 sheets.)
   Here we start with 240 school papers and ask how many *reams* of paper will be needed. We are told that *one* school paper is equivalent to 8 sheets; 480 sheets is equivalent to a ream. Hence

   $$240 \text{ papers} \times \frac{8 \text{ sheets}}{1 \text{ paper}} \times \frac{1 \text{ ream}}{480 \text{ sheets}} = 4 \text{ reams.}$$

3. A bottle contains 100 aspirin tablets. Each tablet contains 5 grains of aspirin. How many ounces of aspirin does the bottle contain? (5760 grains equals 1 lb.) Here we have to start with one bottle and end with a certain number of ounces. The work is done as follows:

$$1 \text{ bottle} \times \frac{100 \text{ tablets}}{1 \text{ bottle}} \times \frac{5 \text{ grains}}{1 \text{ tablet}} \times \frac{1 \text{ lb}}{5760 \text{ grains}} \times$$

$$\frac{16 \text{ oz}}{1 \text{ lb}} \doteq 1.4 \text{ oz}.$$

4. The distance from Cologne to Coblenz is 91 kilometers. What is this distance in miles?

   Here we illustrate how to convert from one system of units to another. Moreover, we will not assume a knowledge of the conversion factor between kilometers and miles. We will, however, assume that everyone knows at least one conversion factor between metric and English distances. Suppose that we remember that one inch is equivalent to approximately 2.54 centimeters. Then we would proceed as follows:

$$91 \text{ km} \times \frac{1000 \text{ m}}{1 \text{ km}} \times \frac{100 \text{ cm}}{1 \text{ m}} \times \frac{1 \text{ in.}}{2.54 \text{ cm}} \times \frac{1 \text{ ft}}{12 \text{ in.}} \times$$

$$\frac{1 \text{ mi}}{5280 \text{ ft}} \doteq 56.5 \text{ mi}.$$

5. A farmer sells 183 bushels of wheat at $1.43 per bushel and takes his pay in flour at 6.75 cents per pound. How many 100 pound sacks of flour does he receive?

   This illustrates still another type of problem that can be solved easily by paying close attention to the units. Here we begin with 183 bushels of wheat and end with the number of 100 pound sacks of flour. The 183 bushels of wheat are multiplied successively by ratios that behave like one until we arrive at the desired result.

$$183 \text{ bu wheat} \times \frac{\$1.43}{1 \text{ bu wheat}} \times \frac{100 \text{ cents}}{\$1} \times \frac{1 \text{ lb flour}}{6.75 \text{ cents}} \times$$

$$\frac{1 \text{ sack flour}}{100 \text{ lb flour}} \doteq 38.8 \text{ sacks}.$$

## 4. Rounding

In studying numbers we have divided them into various classes or sets. These divisions have always been of the "either-or" type, that is, a number belongs to one class or the other. We have given these classes names and we list them here for convenience.

| Either | Or |
|---|---|
| Positive | Negative |
| Rational | Irrational |
| Prime | Composite |
| Even | Odd |
| Exact | Approximate |

For example, it is not possible for a number to be both prime and composite. Neither can a number be both rational and irrational. In spite of this we continue to see people write nonsense like

$$\sqrt{2} = 1.414$$
$$\sqrt{3} = 1.732$$
$$\pi = 3.1416.$$

In these examples the irrational numbers on the left have been equated to the rational numbers on the right.[1] The equals sign is reserved for those cases in which two numbers which are the same are written in different forms. No equivalence relation can be used to relate numbers which are different.

Since

$$(1.414)^2 = 1.999396,$$
$$(1.732)^2 = 2.999824,$$

and

$$\pi = 3.1415926 \ldots ,$$

it would be correct to write

$$\sqrt{2} > 1.414$$
$$\sqrt{3} > 1.732$$
$$\pi < 3.1416.$$

[1] Recall that a rational number can be represented by either a terminating decimal or an infinite decimal in which groups of numerals repeat, while the decimal form of an irrational number is always an infinite non-repeating decimal.

It is much simpler, however, to write

$$\sqrt{2} \doteq 1.414$$
$$\sqrt{3} \doteq 1.732$$
$$\pi \doteq 3.1416,$$

where the symbol $\doteq$ is read "is approximately equal to."

When we use the approximation 3.1416 for the irrational number 3.1415926... we perform a process known as **rounding**. The word may have been derived from the fact that the numerals 9, 2, 6, and all numerals which follow have been changed to zeros in 3.1416, that is, the numerals have been "rounded." By convention, the last digit retained is either *unchanged* or *increased by one* depending on the first digit dropped. If the first digit dropped is greater than four, then one convention is to increase by one the last digit retained. In the above example we changed the 5 to a 6 in the ten-thousandth's place because the first digit dropped was 9.

When increasing a number in the process of rounding it may happen that more than one retained number is changed because of "carrying." If the last digit retained is 9, then increasing this by one will result in a zero in that place. According to convention this zero is written, in order that it will be clear how the number was rounded. For example, to round 1.6972 to two decimal places we would write 1.70.

The process of rounding is not difficult as long as we keep in mind that all decisions are made at the place where the rounding occurs. It might be helpful to draw a vertical line at this point. To illustrate this idea suppose the problem is to round 23.649 to one decimal place. We write this number as

$$23.6 \mid 49$$

and reason as follows: the first digit dropped (to the right of the vertical line) is 4 and, since this digit is *not* greater than 4, we keep the last retained digit (to the left of the vertical line) unchanged. Hence 23.6 is the rounded number. Note that we do *not* write zeros in place of the dropped digits.

As another example, to round 92 569 672 to millions we would write

$$92 \mid 569\,672.$$

Since the first digit dropped is 5, which *is* greater than 4, we change the last digit retained from 2 to 3. The rounded number is 93 000 000 and, in this case, we had to write the zeros. We again stress the fact that the digits 6, 9, 6, 7, 2 were not considered in the above rounding process.

We should mention that there are other conventions used for rounding than the one presented here. Some of these are found in connection with business, banking, federal income tax returns and computers.

## Exercises 13

1. Write each of the following sentences with mathematical symbols.
   (a) Five is two more than three.
   (b) A number is at most seven.
   (c) Twelve is a multiple of three.
   (d) The set of multiples of three is equivalent to the set of multiples of four.
   (e) The set of positive integers and the set of negative integers are disjoint sets.

2. Express each of the following mathematical sentences, with a *minimum* of mathematical symbols, in an English sentence:
   (a) $^-2 < 5$
   (b) $2 \leq n \leq 10$
   (c) $AC \perp AD$
   (d) $\triangle BCD \sim \triangle ECF$
   (e) $12 \div (4 + 3) \neq (12 \div 4) + (12 \div 3)$.

3. Which of the following sentences are true?
   (a) $6 + 7 > 10$
   (b) $3 \leq \frac{6}{2}$
   (c) $^-2 + (^-5) = ^-3$
   (d) $\overleftrightarrow{AB} = \overleftrightarrow{BA}$
   (e) $0 \times 5 = 5$.

4. In each of the following sentences, replace the indefinite pronoun by a proper name that makes the statement true.
   (a) It is the capital of New York.
   (b) He is the author of this book.
   (c) It is the largest state in the United States.
   (d) She was the founder of the Red Cross.
   (e) It is a foreign country.

5. In each statement following, replace the letter by the number that makes the statement true.
   (a) $x - (^-3) = 5$
   (b) $3 \div y = 0.75$
   (c) $2^z = 32$
   (d) $(16)_{10} = (31)_q$
   (e) $10^5 \div 10^2 = 10^p$.

6. Find the solution set of the following:
   (a) $n - 2 < 5$ and $n$ is an integer.
   (b) $3 < n < 7$ and $n$ is a negative integer.
   (c) $n^2 = n^3$ and $n$ is a number.
   (d) $1 + n \leq 5$ and $n$ is a positive integer.
   (e) $3 \times r = 0$.

7. A school furnishes 8 pencils a year to each of its 360 pupils. How many gross of pencils are needed a year?

8. If each one of 25 children at Lakeview School drinks one-half pint of milk every day at school for 16 weeks, how many gallons of milk will they use?

9. A fuse contains $2\frac{1}{2}$ ounces of black powder. How many fuses can be made from 250 pounds of powder?

10. I find that my car can make a trip of 432 miles on $29\frac{1}{2}$ gallons of gasoline. At 32.9 cents a gallon how much will gasoline cost to make a trip of 2385 miles?

11. Round 27.0649 to two decimals; to one decimal; to tens.

12. Round 245 679 to ten thousands; to hundred thousands.

13. Round 0.07849 to three decimals; to two decimals; to one decimal.

14. Compute $2.67 \times 3.82$ and round the answer to one decimal; round the given numbers to one decimal, then multiply and round the answer to one decimal. Compare the two results.

# 14/Arithmetic Operations

## 1. Rules of the game

Although we prefer to call it modern *mathematics* for the elementary school, the fact remains that most of what we teach at this level is *arithmetic*. We don't want to give the impression that arithmetic is some elementary or insignificant form of mathematics, however. In fact, we subscribe to the philosophy that mathematics is the queen of the sciences and, as the great mathematician Karl F. Gauss (1777–1855) stated, that arithmetic is the queen of mathematics.

Number theory has been for centuries, and continues to be today, a source of much research in mathematics. In this branch of mathematics, arithmetic plays an important role. Hence we believe that arithmetic should be given the proper emphasis in the elementary school. This cannot be done by reducing arithmetic to the memorization of various short cut procedures and the use of "gimmicks" which are designed to increase speed of computation but which, in reality, decrease understanding.

In order that students may develop a firm foundation in mathematics we must begin with a clear understanding of the "ground rules." These are provided by the properties (or laws, or axioms) of the particular set of numbers with which we are working. In the elementary school we work only with the real number system.

Recall that the set of real numbers includes the positive and negative irrational numbers, the positive and negative rational numbers and zero. The set of positive rational numbers contains the set of natural (or counting) numbers as a proper subset.

For convenience we assign numbers to the various properties and use **A** to designate the properties for addition, **M** for multiplication, and **D** for a combination of the two. Following are the properties of the real numbers:

**A1.** The sum of any two real numbers is again a real number. That is, $a + b = c$ where $a$, $b$, and $c$ are real numbers. (Closure property).

**A2.** The order in which addition is performed is immaterial. That is, $a + b = b + a$ for any real numbers $a$ and $b$. (Commutative property).

**A3.** Three numbers can be added by grouping pairs in any manner whatever. That is, $(a + b) + c = a + (b + c)$ where $a$, $b$, and $c$ are any real numbers. (Associative property).

**A4.** Adding zero to any real number leaves that number unchanged. That is, $a + 0 = a$ for every real number $a$. (Additive identity).

**A5.** Every real number has an opposite. That is, to every real number $a$ there corresponds a real number $(^-a)$ which has the property that $a + (^-a) = 0$. (Additive inverse).

**M1.** The product of any two real numbers is again a real number. That is, $a \times b = c$, where $a$, $b$, and $c$ are real numbers. (Closure property).

**M2.** The order in which multiplication is performed is immaterial. That is, $a \times b = b \times a$ for any real numbers $a$ and $b$. (Commutative property).

**M3.** Three numbers can be multiplied by grouping pairs in any manner whatever. That is, $(a \times b) \times c = a \times (b \times c)$ where $a$, $b$, and $c$ are any real numbers. (Associative property).

**M4.** Multiplying any real number by one leaves that number unchanged. That is, $a \times 1 = a$ for every real number $a$. (Multiplicative identity).

**M5.** Every nonzero real number has a reciprocal. That is, to every nonzero real number $a$ there corresponds a real number $a^{-1}$ which has the property that $a \times a^{-1} = 1$. (Multiplicative inverse).

**D.** Multiplication of real numbers can be distributed over addition. That is, $a \times (b + c) = (a \times b) + (a \times c)$ for any real numbers $a$, $b$, and $c$. (Distributive property).

All this is implied by the term "the real number system." By this we mean the set of real numbers *and* two well-defined[1] operations + and ×, *and* the eleven properties above.

We have already discussed the arithmetic operations as applied to integers. Note that when we say "integers," we mean positive and negative integers and zero. If we want to talk about positive integers only, we will use the modifying adjective. The same holds true of rational numbers, irrational numbers, and real numbers. All these terms imply *both* positive and negative.

## 2. Decimal numbers

A decimal number is a number of the form 327.654. A consideration of *place value* tells us that this is equivalent to

$$(3 \times 10^2) + (2 \times 10) + (7 \times 1) + (6 \times 1/10) + (5 \times 1/100) + (4 \times 1/1000).$$

There are many plus signs here but one is shown heavier than the others. This one, read "and," corresponds to the decimal point in 327.654.

If we used exponent notation throughout, the number would be written

$$(3 \times 10^2) + (2 \times 10^1) + (7 \times 1) + (6 \times 1/10^1) + (5 \times 1/10^2) + (4 \times 1/10^3).$$

It is natural, therefore, to *define* $10^0$ as 1, $10^{-1}$ as $1/10^1$, $10^{-2}$ as $1/10^2$, $10^{-3}$ as $1/10^3$, and so forth. Thus,

$$327.654 = (3 \times 10^2) + (2 \times 10^1) + (7 \times 10^0) + (6 \times 10^{-1}) + (5 \times 10^{-2}) + (4 \times 10^{-3}).$$

Note that the exponents come from the set of integers.

You should check that the negative exponents obey the same rules as the positive exponents. Positive exponents enable us to express very large numbers conveniently while negative exponents enable us to express very small numbers with ease. For example,

[1] A binary operation o is said to be well defined (or unambiguous) if, whenever $a = a'$ and $b = b'$, then $aob = a'ob'$. This is also equivalent to saying that the operation has the *uniqueness property*.

$$93\ 000\ 000 = 9.3 \times 10^7 = 93 \text{ million,}$$
$$1\ 000\ 000\ 000 = 1 \times 10^9 = 10^9 = 1 \text{ billion,}$$
$$.000032 = 3.2 \times 10^{-5} = 32 \text{ millionths,}$$
$$.0000001 = 1 \times 10^{-7} = 10^{-7} = 1 \text{ ten millionth.}$$

If there is a question about $10^0$ and why this is defined as 1, it can be easily answered by the following example. We know that

$$10^5/10^3 = \frac{10 \times 10 \times 10 \times 10 \times 10}{10 \times 10 \times 10} = 10^2.$$

In other words $10^5/10^3 = 10^{5-3} = 10^2$. Similarly, $10^4/10^4 = 10^{4-4} = 10^0$ but we know $10^4/10^4 = 1$. Hence defining $10^0$ as 1 gives us a consistent system.

The student's first experience with decimal numbers could be in multiplication. We consider examples like $32.3 \times 17$ and $46 \times 7.8$. We do not give any rules about where to put the decimal point in the product. Instead we encourage students to *discover* where the decimal point should be placed by reasoning that $32.3 \times 17$ is almost like $30 \times 20$ or 600. Thus if we multiply 323 (ignoring the decimal point) by 17 we get 5491 and it is obvious that this should be written as 549.1.

In the case of $46 \times 7.8$ we consider $46 \times 78$ and get 3588. Estimating, we know the product must be between $40 \times 8 = 320$ and $50 \times 8 = 400$ so that we have no difficulty in arriving at 358.8. This procedure not only has the advantage that the student discovers the correct rule for himself but it also encourages him to *estimate* the result.

This idea can be developed by considering products like $32 \times 7.38$ and $27 \times 6.215$. The first of these is close to $30 \times 7$ or 210 and the second to $30 \times 6$ or 180. Hence when we multiply 32 by 738 and obtain 23 616, we have no difficulty in placing the decimal point to obtain 236.16. In the second case we compute $27 \times 6215$ to get 167 805 and it is obvious that this must be 167.805.

By now all but the slowest students have an intuitive idea about the placing of the decimal point. Drill in today's mathematics serves not only to develop skills but also to help make discoveries.

The teacher should then confirm the discovery by pointing out that

$$32 \times 7.38 = 32 \times 7\frac{38}{100}$$

$$= 32 \times \left(7 + \frac{38}{100}\right)$$

$$= (32 \times 7) + \left(32 \times \frac{38}{100}\right)$$

$$= 224 + \frac{1216}{100}$$

$$= 224 + 12.16$$

$$= 236.16.$$

In other words, because of the presence of hundredths in the multiplier 7.38, it is inevitable that hundredths should also appear in the product 236.16.

Similarly, the second example when expanded, using the properties of real numbers, produces

$$27 \times 6.215 = 27 \times \left(6 + \frac{215}{1000}\right)$$

$$= (27 \times 6) + \left(27 \times \frac{215}{1000}\right)$$

$$= 162 + \frac{5805}{1000}$$

$$= 162 + 5.805$$

$$= 167.805.$$

Just as a number has many names, there are many ways to perform an arithmetic operation.

We extend multiplication to products like $32.2 \times 16.24$. First, we estimate: $30 \times 16 = 480$; then multiply 322 by 1624 to obtain 522 928 which is then written 522.928. Next we strengthen the concept by computing

$$32.2 \times 16.24 = \left(32 + \frac{2}{10}\right) \times \left(16 + \frac{24}{100}\right)$$

$$= (32 \times 16) + \left(32 + \frac{24}{100}\right) + \left(\frac{2}{10} \times 16\right) + \left(\frac{2}{10} \times \frac{24}{100}\right)$$

$$= 512 + \frac{768}{100} + \frac{32}{10} + \frac{48}{1000}$$

$$= 512 + 7.68 + 3.2 + .048$$
$$= 522.928.$$

The presence of the term 48/1000 indicates that we obtain *thousandths* when we multiply a number containing *tenths* by one containing *hundredths*.

Another way to illustrate this is the following:

$$32.2 \times 16.24 = 32\frac{2}{10} \times 16\frac{24}{100}$$
$$= \frac{322}{10} \times \frac{1624}{100}$$
$$= \frac{522\,928}{1000}$$
$$= 522.928.$$

The more a teacher knows about mathematics, the more ways he can illustrate a concept and thus reach more students. It is hardly possible to give students an understanding of mathematics if the teacher knows only certain rules and algorithms.

In another system of numeration we have a similar situation. For example, in the octal system we consider the product,

$$(7.2)_8 \times (16.5)_8.$$

We know $(72)_8 \times (165)_8 = (15202)_8$, hence we write the product as $(152.02)_8$. Note that the *octal point* is placed in exactly the same manner as the decimal point. An analogous procedure is used with the binary point, the quinary point and the duodecimal point. There is no limit in the new approach to mathematics as far as inspiring the talented student is concerned.

We call attention to the fact that applying exponents to a base is a characteristic of any system of numeration. For example,

$$(237.65)_8 = (2 \times 8^2) + (3 \times 8^1) + (7 \times 8^0) + (6 \times 8^{-1}) + (5 \times 8^{-2}).$$

This now allows us to convert the octal numeral 237.65 to its decimal equivalent as follows:

$$(237.65)_8 = 128 + 24 + 7 + \frac{6}{8} + \frac{5}{64}$$
$$= (159.828125)_{10}.$$

We invite you to verify this conversion and to contemplate the reverse procedure, that is, changing a decimal number to octal.

The ancient Romans did not know about decimal numbers and they were burdened with a cumbersome system of numeration as well. When they were faced with the problem of deciding how XX out of XXV compared with XXXIII out of XL, they reasoned as follows:

20 out of 25 is the same as 80 out of 100,
33 out of 40 is the same as $82\frac{1}{2}$ out of 100.

Hence 33 out of 40 is *greater than* 20 out of 25. By converting everything to so much *per hundred* it was easy to compare various ratios. They called "per hundred" **per cent** and we still use this term (currently written as one word, *percent*, and represented by the symbol %).

To change the ratio 4/5 to percent we ask, "Four out of five is how many out of a hundred?" In other words,

$$\frac{4}{5} = \frac{?}{100}.$$

The missing number is easily found by using the proper form of the multiplicative identity.

$$\frac{4}{5} = \frac{4}{5} \times 1 = \frac{4}{5} \times \frac{20}{20} = \frac{80}{100} = 80\%.$$

Note carefully that there are no rules, no gimmicks! We use only the definition of percent and the properties of real numbers. We illustrate with several more examples.

$$\frac{3}{4} = \frac{3}{4} \times 1 = \frac{3}{4} \times \frac{25}{25} = \frac{75}{100} = 75\%$$

$$\frac{3}{40} = \frac{3}{40} \times \frac{2\frac{1}{2}}{2\frac{1}{2}} = \frac{7\frac{1}{2}}{100} = 7\frac{1}{2}\%$$

$$\frac{3}{400} = \frac{3}{400} \times \frac{\frac{1}{4}}{\frac{1}{4}} = \frac{\frac{3}{4}}{100} = \frac{3}{4}\%$$

$$3 = \frac{3}{1} = \frac{3}{1} \times \frac{100}{100} = \frac{300}{100} = 300\%$$

$$\frac{3}{8} = \frac{3}{8} \times \frac{12\frac{1}{2}}{12\frac{1}{2}} = \frac{37\frac{1}{2}}{100} = 37\frac{1}{2}\%.$$

**Arithmetic Operations**

Of course it requires some thought to find the proper form of the multiplicative identity. How did we know, for example, that $2\frac{1}{2}/2\frac{1}{2}$ was the correct form in the second example above? Because the question was: what must you multiply 40 by to get 100? This is the same as asking: what is 100 divided by 40? Try this with the last example above and see if you get $12\frac{1}{2}/12\frac{1}{2}$.

Combining our knowledge of percent notation with decimal notation makes it easy to express numbers in various forms. In the second example above we could have written $7\frac{1}{2}\%$ as 7.5%, or in the third example $\frac{3}{4}\%$ can be expressed as .75%.

Converting from percent notation to any other form is simple if you reverse the steps in the above examples. By way of illustration,

$$35\% = \frac{35}{100} = \frac{35}{100} \div \frac{5}{5} = \frac{7}{20} \quad \text{or}$$

$$35\% = \frac{35}{100} = .35$$

$$4.85\% = \frac{4.85}{100} = \frac{4.85}{100} \times \frac{100}{100} = \frac{485}{10\ 000} = .0485$$

$$500\% = \frac{500}{100} = \frac{500}{100} \div \frac{100}{100} = \frac{5}{1} = 5$$

$$.08\% = \frac{.08}{100} = \frac{.08}{100} \times \frac{100}{100} = \frac{8}{10\ 000} = .0008.$$

Note that we do not "move the decimal point" to the right or to the left! We use definitions and properties of numbers, and we let the students discover the short cuts. After some drill a student will be able to write .0008 for .08%, omitting the intermediate steps. However, if he is challenged, he will be able to fill in the logical steps.

In view of the above, we fail to see why percent was formerly taught in the fifth grade and again in the sixth grade, reviewed in the seventh and eighth grades, and taught again in the ninth grade. In most colleges, students majoring in business get another dose of percent. Yet after all this, if you ask the average person what is meant by the sign, "All suits reduced 40%," he will be hard put to give an intelligent answer. This is the type of thing we are trying to eliminate by changing our methods of teaching mathematics.

While multiplication of decimal numbers was easy to comprehend, division is more difficult because the inverses of the basic mathematical processes are generally more involved. We begin by dividing a decimal number by a counting number. For example, 65.3 ÷ 22. Again we estimate the result and it is no trick to see that the quotient is approximately 3. Dividing 653 (ignoring the decimal point) by 22 gives 2968+ and it is obvious that the quotient is 2.968+ where the plus sign indicates that there is a remainder at this point. Division affords an excellent opportunity for teaching rounding.

After many such exercises students will discover that the decimal point in the quotient is *directly above* the decimal point in the dividend in long division.

We can now advance to the more difficult case, that is, where we have to divide 65.3 by 2.6. We solve this problem by reducing it to something we already know. For example,

$$65.3 \div 2.6 = \frac{65.3}{2.6} = \frac{65.3}{2.6} \times 1 = \frac{65.3}{2.6} \times \frac{10}{10} = \frac{653}{26}$$

and there is no problem in performing the last division. As another example,

$$27.87 \div 3.5 = \frac{27.87}{3.5} = \frac{27.87}{3.5} \times \frac{10}{10} = \frac{278.7}{35}$$

and this can be done in the manner previously explained. Finally,

$$.067 \div .0009 = \frac{.067}{.0009} \times \frac{10\ 000}{10\ 000} = \frac{670}{9}.$$

Thus we can reduce every problem involving division of decimals to one involving division of a decimal by a counting number.

## Exercises 14

1. State the property **D** of real numbers after applying property **M2**.

2. Explain how four real numbers could be added by using the properties of the real number system.

3. Explain how five real numbers could be multiplied by using the properties of the real number system.

4. Show how the distributive property still applies when there are three addends.

5. Estimate $2.73 \div 0.46$.

6. Explain how to perform the division of exercise 5.

7. Estimate $80.7 \times 4.132$.

8. Explain how to perform the multiplication of exercise 7.

9. Change 0.0485 to percent.

10. Change $(23)_5$ to percent.

11. What is 0.001% expressed as a fraction?

12. What is 385% expressed as a number in the quinary system?

13. Which is greater, $^{19}\!/_{46}$ or $^{20}\!/_{47}$?

14. Which is greater, 0.999 . . . or 1?

15. Which is smaller, 4.33333 or $4\frac{1}{3}$?

16. Change $(23.5)_8$ to the decimal system of numeration.

17. Convert $(12.36)_{10}$ to the octal system of numeration.

18. Verify that $14.3 \times 43.2 = 1344.31$ in the quinary system of numeration.

19. Check exercise 18 by converting all the numbers to the decimal system of numeration.

20. Explain how to divide 110.01 by 11.1 where these numbers are expressed in the binary system of numeration.

# 15/Supplementary Work

## 1. Magic squares

There is a definite place for mathematical recreations in modern mathematics teaching. Unfortunately, some teachers have acquired the mistaken notion that modern mathematics teaching consists solely of making a game out of mathematics. They reason that since in the past it was largely a matter of drudgery and consequently hated, we must now emphasize the recreational aspects. Nothing could be farther from the truth! Mathematics is serious business at every grade level, and it requires concentrated thinking to achieve mastery.

Recreation has its place in mathematics in providing some relief from the serious aspects and in serving to disguise the drill work. We have already stressed that providing variety in drillwork is one way to make mathematics more palatable. In some respects mathematics is like cod liver oil—it's awfully good for you but it needs to be mixed with orange juice to keep it down. Recreational mathematics is the orange juice in this case.

*Magic squares* are always interesting. They come in various types and sizes. Some contain integers, others have fractions, and still others have both positive and negative numbers.

A simple magic square is the following one:

| 8 | 1 | 6 |
|---|---|---|
| 3 | 5 | 7 |
| 4 | 9 | 2 |

Here all three rows, all three columns, and both diagonals add to 15. Another one is:

| | | | |
|---|---|---|---|
| 16 | 2 | 3 | 13 |
| 5 | 11 | 10 | 8 |
| 9 | 7 | 6 | 12 |
| 4 | 14 | 15 | 1 |

Here the "magic" sum is 34. A feature of magic squares is that no numbers are repeated. For example, the $3 \times 3$ magic square uses the numbers from 1 to 9 inclusive, the $4 \times 4$ square uses the numbers from 1 to 16 inclusive, etc.

A famous magic square is one called "Nasik" which is carved in Sanskrit characters on the gate of a fort in India.

| | | | |
|---|---|---|---|
| 15 | 10 | 3 | 6 |
| 4 | 5 | 16 | 9 |
| 14 | 11 | 2 | 7 |
| 1 | 8 | 13 | 12 |

This has all the properties of the previous $4 \times 4$ square, namely, rows, columns, and diagonals add to 34, but all adjacent $2 \times 2$ squares also add to 34. For example, $15 + 10 + 5 + 4$ and $5 + 16 + 2 + 11$ and

3 + 6 + 9 + 16 all add to 34. Can you find the 25 different ways in which this remarkable square gives a sum of 34?

Another unusual magic square is the following one:

| 1 | 23 | 137 | 223 | 263 |
| 167 | 229 | 191 | 7 | 53 |
| 197 | 37 | 83 | 173 | 157 |
| 89 | 101 | 163 | 227 | 67 |
| 193 | 257 | 73 | 17 | 107 |

Here, not only are all the entries except one prime numbers, but the sum 647 is also a prime.

A variation of the magic square is the following magic circle:

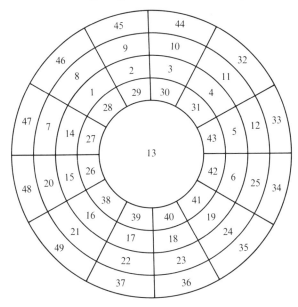

Here the sum of the numbers along any one of the 12 diameters is 215. But even more remarkable is the fact that this sum will remain unchanged if any one (or more) of the rings is revolved to any position. Have one of your students make one out of cardboard and try it!

There are a number of ways to use magic squares for drill. In the earlier grades students can be given $3 \times 3$ and $4 \times 4$ squares and asked to find the "magic" number. In order to make the work interesting, the teacher can occasionally change one of the numbers in the square so that it loses its magic quality. Children will be delighted to discover that a particular square is not magic after all!

Later, more difficult magic squares can be used. By this we mean not only $5 \times 5$ and $6 \times 6$ and larger, but also squares that contain fractions and both positive and negative numbers. There are also some that involve other operations, such as multiplication. For the unusually talented student there are also magic cubes! A good source of magic squares and cubes is a book by Andrews.[1] A simple explanation of how magic squares can be constructed has been given by Merrill.[2]

## 2. Puzzles and patterns

One of the characteristics of modern mathematics teaching is that the essential drill work is disguised as much as possible. An excellent way to get the necessary drill accomplished, and make it fun at the same time, is to use puzzles.

One of the puzzles that can be used in the intermediate grades is the following: "Take a number, multiply it by 3, add 12, divide by 3, subtract 4. The final result should be the original number." This is an interesting puzzle because it uses all four of the arithmetic operations. Many teachers are using it with good results.

However, a perplexing question arises from this simple puzzle. The question is, "All four arithmetic operations are used and I know that two of these are inverses of the other two. Hence I can see why one needs to divide by 3 after having first multiplied by 3. This certainly restores the status quo. But how can subtracting 4 neutralize adding 12?"

[1] Andrews, W. S., *Magic Squares and Cubes*, Dover Publications, Inc., New York 1960.
[2] Merrill, H. A., *Mathematical Excursions*, Dover Publications, Inc., New York, 1957, pp. 67–76.

On the face of it, something is not quite right here. By taking a *general* problem, however, it is possible to get at the truth. Let the original number be denoted by $n$. When we multiply by 3, we get $3n$. Adding 12 produces $3n + 12$ and dividing this by 3 yields $n + 4$. (Note that $3n + 12$ can be written as $3(n + 4)$ by the distributive property and dividing this by 3 gives $n + 4$.) Finally, subtracting 4 from $n + 4$ brings us back to the original number $n$. Looking at the above process carefully reveals the "secret"—if it can be dignified with such a name.

Once the above process is understood a variety of puzzles can be designed. For example, "Take a number, multiply it by 5, add 15, divide by 5, subtract 3 and you will have the original number."

It should be noted that there are no restrictions on the original number in puzzles of this type. The number may be positive, zero, negative, in the fractional or decimal form. Thus, for students in grades 5 and 6, we might pose the problem: "Take a number between zero and one, multiply it by 4, add 8, divide by 4, subtract 2 and you will end with the original number." Or: "Take a negative number, multiply it by 7, add 21, divide by 7, and subtract 3."

There are a great variety of number patterns which can be used to stimulate interest and to teach mathematics. We list a number of these.

$$1 = 1 = 1^2$$
$$1 + 3 = 4 = 2^2$$
$$1 + 3 + 5 = 9 = 3^2$$
$$1 + 3 + 5 + 7 = 16 = 4^2$$
$$1 + 3 + 5 + 7 + 9 = 25 = 5^2$$
$$1 + 3 + 5 + 7 + 9 + 11 = 36 = 6^2$$
$$\text{etc.}$$

$$1 \cdot = 1 = \frac{2 \times 1}{2}$$

$$1 + 2 = 3 = \frac{3 \times 2}{2}$$

$$1 + 2 + 3 = 6 = \frac{4 \times 3}{2}$$

$$1 + 2 + 3 + 4 = 10 = \frac{5 \times 4}{2}$$

$$1 + 2 + 3 + 4 + 5 \qquad = 15 = \frac{6 \times 5}{2}$$

$$1 + 2 + 3 + 4 + 5 + 6 \qquad = 21 = \frac{7 \times 6}{2}$$

$$1 + 2 + 3 + 4 + 5 + 6 + 7 = 28 = \frac{8 \times 7}{2}$$

etc.

$$
\begin{aligned}
2 &= 2 = 1 \times 2 \\
2 + 4 &= 6 = 2 \times 3 \\
2 + 4 + 6 &= 12 = 3 \times 4 \\
2 + 4 + 6 + 8 &= 20 = 4 \times 5 \\
2 + 4 + 6 + 8 + 10 &= 30 = 5 \times 6 \\
2 + 4 + 6 + 8 + 10 + 12 &= 42 = 6 \times 7
\end{aligned}
$$

etc.

$$
\begin{aligned}
2^0 &= 1 = 2 - 1 = 2^1 - 1 \\
2^0 + 2 &= 3 = 4 - 1 = 2^2 - 1 \\
2^0 + 2 + 2^2 &= 7 = 8 - 1 = 2^3 - 1 \\
2^0 + 2 + 2^2 + 2^3 &= 15 = 16 - 1 = 2^4 - 1 \\
2^0 + 2 + 2^2 + 2^3 + 2^4 &= 31 = 32 - 1 = 2^5 - 1
\end{aligned}
$$

etc.

More difficult patterns may be found in any algebra book under the heading of "mathematical induction." This topic is concerned with finding and proving a general formula.


## 3. Self-evaluation for the brave

Now that you have been exposed to a certain amount of modern mathematics the question naturally arises whether this exposure has had any effect. In other words, have you caught the spirit of modern mathematics? The following test questions will help you to determine how well you have mastered the ABC's of modern mathematics.

1. What do the following have in common: circle, line, angle, polygon?

2. $\{1, 2, 3, 4, 5, \ldots\}$ is the set of _____ numbers.

**3.** ¾, 3.1416, −3, 0, are all _____ numbers.

**4.** $a/b$ is the form of a rational number. The number $b$ may be: (a) zero sometimes   (b) anything   (c) a counting number   (d) a real number.

**5.** A quadrilateral is a (a) plane   (b) line   (c) polygon   (d) square.

**6.** Which of the following is not a prime number? (a) 1   (b) 2   (c) 3   (d) 5   (e) none of these.

**7.** _____ is the _____ of _____ and _____. (This is not a facetious question! Fill in the blanks with *mathematical* terms).

**8.** A curve is a line. True or false?

**9.** The measure of anything is _____.

**10.** A square is a parallelogram. True or false?

**11.** The set of rational numbers is a proper subset of the set of _____ numbers.

**12.** In finding the sum of $\frac{3}{12}$ and $\frac{9}{12}$ we are using the _____ property of numbers.

**13.** Why is ½ equal to $\frac{3}{6}$?

**14.** The number zero is (a) an odd number   (b) an even number   (c) not a number   (d) none of these.

**15.** What do the following have in common? (a) centimeter   (b) inch   (c) yard   (d) mile.

**16.** A polyhedron is a figure in _____-dimensional geometry.

**17.** The center of a circle lies on the circle. True or false?

**18.** If $A = \{2, 1, 5, 8, 10\}$ and $B = \{0, 3, 2, 6, 9, 5\}$, then $A \cap B =$ _____.

**19.** In the previous problem, $A \cup B =$ _____.

**20.** If $A = \{$even numbers$\}$ and $B = \{$odd numbers$\}$, what is $A \cap B$?

**21.** What does $(34)_5$ mean?

**22.** Give three pairs of twin primes.

**Supplementary Work**

**23.** What property of numbers is illustrated in the following:

$$
\begin{array}{r}
23 \\
17 \\
\hline
161 \\
230 \\
\hline
391
\end{array}
$$

**24.** What do the letters SMSG represent?

**25.** A plane is (a) a line   (b) a solid   (c) a surface   (d) a polyhedron
(e) an isosceles trapezoid.

**26.** In your opinion what is the *single* characteristic that *best* describes
the "new" mathematics?

**27.** The divisors of 60 are _____.

**28.** Why is zero called an annihilator?

**29.** Which of the following are irrational numbers (a) $\sqrt{3}$ (b) 3.1416
(c) 1.333 . . . (d) $3\sqrt{2}$ (e) ¾.

**30.** Given the following triangle:

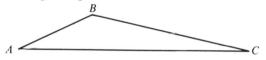

(a) Mark $\angle ABC$ with a wavy line.
(b) Circle the vertex $C$.
(c) Indicate $AC$.

**31.** Which number is larger: $\sqrt{10}$ or 3.1623?

**32.** Which of the two numbers in question 31 is a rational number?
Why?

**33.** If $A$ is the set of college students who are taking a history course,
how would you describe $A'$?

**34.** Consider the following Venn diagram:

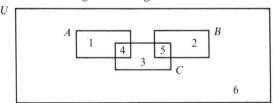

Indicate the answers to the following using appropriate numbers.

$A \cap C :$_____; $A \cap B :$_____;

$B \cup C :$_____; $(A \cup B)' :$_____;

$C' :$_____.

**35.** Find $\sqrt{92}$ to two decimal places by using the Heroian algorithm.

**36.** Complementation is a (unary) (binary) operation.

**37.** Forming the intersection of sets is a (unary) (binary) operation.

**38.** Finding the square root of a number is a (unary) (binary) operation.

**39.** What law (or property) is exhibited in the following?

$$A \cap (B \cup C) = (A \cap B) \cup (A \cap C).$$

**40.** Perform the following division by the modern method:

$$3753 \div 85$$

**41.** What name is given to the number one?

**42.** What property of rational numbers is exhibited here?

$$\frac{a}{b} \times \frac{c}{d} = \frac{c}{d} \times \frac{a}{b}$$

**43.** Find the GCD of 104 and 130 using the Euclidean algorithm.

**44.** What name is given to the number zero?

**45.** In order to find the area of a trapezoid it is necessary to know how to find the areas of _____.

**46.** What is the solution set of the equation: $2x - 5 = x + 2$?

**47.** Make a factor tree for factoring 264 into prime factors.

**48.** Express the prime factors of 264 in exponent form.

**49.** Change $(3704)_8$ to decimal notation.

**50.** Change $(245)_{10}$ to binary notation.

**51.** If $A$ and $B$ are sets, and if $n(A) = n(B)$, we say $A$ and $B$ are

_____.

**52.** If $A$ and $B$ are sets, then $n(A \cup B)$ is the same as $n(A) + n(B)$ less _____.

**53.** If $A$ and $B$ are sets, then $n(A \cap B)$ is at least _____.

**54.** Write the number 16 as follows:

    (a) Using addition _____

    (b) Using subtraction _____

    (c) Using multiplication _____

    (d) Using division _____

    (e) Using exponent notation _____

    (f) Using Roman numerals _____

    (g) Using a foreign language _____

    (h) Using square root _____

    (i) Using percent _____

    (j) Using the distributive law _____

    (k) Using base 5 _____

    (l) One other way different from the above _____.

**55.** Every even number which is divisible by 7 is also divisible by _____.

**56.** The "sieve of Eratosthenes" is a method for finding _____ numbers.

**57.** There (are) (are not) infinitely many multiples of three.

**58.** There (are) (are not) as many multiples of 100 as there are even numbers.

**59.** Equivalent sets are equal. True or false?

**60.** On how many basic rules does the arithmetic of real numbers depend?

**61.** On what basic operations does the arithmetic of real numbers depend?

**62.** Explain the following addition problem using the number line: $3 + (^-2)$.

**63.** What do the following have in common? $2^0$, $8^0$, $5^0$

**64.** What name is given to the "point" in the following number: $(3.67)_8$?

**65.** Place the proper sign ($<$, $>$, $=$) between the following pairs of numbers:

(a) 2.237 _____ $\sqrt{5}$

(b) 81 _____ $3^4$

(c) $\sqrt{2}$ _____ 1.414

(d) 0.3333 _____ $\frac{1}{3}$

(e) $3\frac{2}{5}$ _____ 320%

**66.** What is wrong with the following statement? The sum of two consecutive odd numbers is 35.

**67.** Another name for $\frac{9}{5}$ is _____.

**68.** Using only the terms positive integer, negative integer, positive rational number, negative rational number, positive irrational number, negative irrational number, zero, identify the following numbers:

(a) 1.4 _____

(b) 3.1416 _____

(c) $\sqrt{2}$ _____

(d) $\dfrac{\sqrt{3}}{-2}$ _____

(e) 17 _____

(f) 0 _____

(g) $\dfrac{-15}{-3}$ _____

(h) $\dfrac{22}{7}$ _____

(i) $\dfrac{0}{-7}$ _____

If you have answered the above questions more or less correctly you may consider yourself as having mastered the ABC's of modern mathematics. Congratulations! Remember that the DEF's, the GHI's, and so on still lie ahead of you! We hope that you have been challenged to attack these greater heights!

As a further test of your knowledge, the following are some questions and answers gleaned from various examinations over a period of many years. The answers may be classified as student "boners." The object is to determine what the correct answer is and also to analyze the answer given and determine where it fails. The students' answers are unedited except for spelling and gross punctuation errors.

**Question:** Explain and illustrate the special properties of the number zero.

*Answer:* Zero is significant in some operations and not so significant in others. The "0" when used in addition is the additive identity, since adding 0 to other addends does not affect the sum. The use of 0 in division and multiplication is not as significant, because multiplying or dividing anything by 0 will equal nothing.

*Answer:* Zero added to, subtracted from, multiplied times something, or divided into something will not change the properties of that thing.

*Answer:* Zero is the additive identity in addition. Whatever is added to zero will always come out zero. $0 + 3 = 0$.

**Question:** What is the meaning of "exponent?" How are exponents used in mathematics?

*Answer:* (a) Exponent represents a given number telling you to multiply another number that many times by itself. Example. $4^3 = 4 \times 4 \times 4 = 64$.

(b) Shortens addition and it shortens multiplication. Exponents can be cancelled out when doing a problem.

$$\frac{6^4}{12^6} = \frac{3}{6^2} \text{ etc.}$$

**Question:** Attack or defend this statement: It is just as important for girls to obtain a knowledge of mathematics as it is for boys.

*Answer:* I would say that it is. First of all, women are going into every field that a man is, except maybe trying to be another Willie Shoemaker. Seriously though, a woman goes shopping, she goes walking, she budgets the money etc. so she needs to know all these things. She needs to know why 2 eight-ounce cans at 10¢ each is more economical than an eight-ounce can at 25¢. If she goes walking out of necessity rather than pleasure, she should know that the shortest distance between two points is a straight line. If she is making a bowl of punch she needs to know how many it will serve.

**Question:** Criticize some topic in mathematics from the standpoint of how it was taught to you.

*Answer:* To tell you the truth it seems most of it was taught to be wrong! However, I think if I had been able to associate mathematical concepts with my everyday life it would have helped. Also instead of having to do a certain problem or problems, if I had learned more rules and formulas (and the *why* of them) I would be better able to work any type of problem. Otherwise when you stop dealing with apples and oranges and pies you are lost.

**Question:** Why is $8 - 5 = 3$?

*Answer:* Because in 8 equal parts, when 3 of these 8 are removed, 5 are left because we use the decimal system and in that system 5 is what we finish with. We assume 5 to be correct because much of math is assumption anyhow.

**Question:** What is the difference between V and 5?

*Answer:* The main difference is that the lines in Roman V are straight. This makes it easier to use on buildings, places where it is more convenient to use straight lines.

**Question:** What is zero and how is it used?

*Answer:*   Zero is the first number in our system and extremely important. Our system would collapse without it. It is used to express percent, fractions, whole numbers, etc. It is also used, by itself, to represent nothing. Decimal points make its value change as with any other number but it is a most useful and necessary number or digit.


## 4. Suggestions for further study

Textbooks in mathematics are changing rapidly today. We find that authors and publishers are in a rush to put the "latest in mathematics" on the market. Many school systems are revising their curricula to incorporate some of the recent recommendations of mathematics study groups. All this means that it is quite possible for one to pick up a mathematics book and be unable to understand it although he may have had a course in this particular subject at one time.

Recognizing that many persons have a need to catch up in mathematics, we have prepared a list of books which are especially helpful for this purpose. Whether you are a parent wondering what your children are studying in mathematics, or a teacher worrying about having to relearn everything, or a student about to embark on a new course with a feeling of insecurity, you will find some help in the list. And the best part is that you will be able to study most of these books by yourself. It will require concentration and hard work in some cases but it will be worth it.

1. Allendoerfer, C. B. and C. O. Oakley: FUNDAMENTALS OF FRESHMAN MATHEMATICS, McGraw-Hill, 1959.

This book begins with the number system and ends with hyperbolic functions. The stated purpose of the book is to bridge the gap between intermediate algebra and analytic geometry and calculus. The more difficult problems are marked with an asterisk and some are marked "BT" which means "booby trap." The book is written from a modern viewpoint, and there are good treatments of such subjects as inequalities, sets and matrices.

2. Banks, J. Houston: ELEMENTS OF MATHEMATICS, second edition, Allyn and Bacon, 1961.

This book seeks to develop the fundamental concepts and techniques of mathematics at a level of abstraction appropriate for the college student who has studied no mathematics beyond the secondary school. The book is written in a conversational style which makes it ideally suited for self study. Although the author did not intend this to be a remedial text, it could very well be used by a student who does not have the proper background in mathematics. The book is a very good bridge between the gap that sometimes exists between high school mathematics and college mathematics. The author pays proper attention to the fact that mathematics is a sequential subject.

3. Bell, Clifford, C. D. Hammond, and R. B. Herrera: FUNDA-MENTALS OF ARITHMETIC FOR TEACHERS, John Wiley and Sons, 1962.

One of the principal objectives of this book is to give the student an appreciation for numbers and for operations with them as well as an understanding of the over-all structure of mathematics. Careful attention to problem solving is also a major concern of the book.

4. Combellack, Wilfred J.: INTRODUCTION TO ELEMENTARY FUNCTIONS, John Wiley and Sons, 1962.

This book was written as a one-semester textbook at the precalculus level for students who have a minimum of three years of college preparatory mathematics but who were not exposed to the modern mathematics viewpoint in high school. The author bridges the gap to the study of college mathematics and shows a great deal of sympathy toward the problem of the reader at this level. It is an excellent book and highly recommended.

5. Dutton, Wilbur and L. J. Adams: ARITHMETIC FOR TEACHERS, Prentice-Hall, 1961.

This book presents the teaching of arithmetic from the standpoint of both method and content. From the former standpoint the book is very good. There are a large number of lesson plans given which are in the dialogue form and show the expected responses of the pupils. From the standpoint of content the book is fairly standard. Not much of the new material is included but the old material is very well done. For example, the explanation of the various types of percentage problems is given from the algebraic viewpoint.

6. Evenson, A. B : MODERN MATHEMATICS—INTRODUCTORY CONCEPTS AND THEIR IMPLICATIONS, Scott, Foresman and Company, 1962.

This paperback of 206 pages is a bargain for any teacher or parent who desires to know something about the way mathematics is taught today.

7. Gray, James, F.: SETS, RELATIONS, AND FUNCTIONS, Holt, Rinehart, and Winston, 1962.

This little paperback of 140 pages was written for a television program directed to secondary teachers and students of the greater San Antonio area. The author apologizes for writing such a non-rigorous book which can be read so easily. He need not, however, because many secondary school teachers will be challenged by it. He goes fairly deeply into each of the three topics he discusses.

8. Hacker, Sidney D., Wilfred E. Barnes, and Calvin T. Long: FUNDAMENTAL CONCEPTS OF ARITHMETIC, Prentice-Hall, 1963.

A scholarly but readable book recommended for the reader who wants additional and more detailed information. Systems of numeration based on three and six are included. There is also some interesting discussion relative to the number of primes in various intervals and an excellent discussion of Euclid's proof that there cannot be a largest prime.

9. Herberg, Theodore and James Bristol: ELEMENTARY MATHE-MATICAL ANALYSIS, D. C. Heath, 1962.

This book is essentially an elementary course in functions designed to supplement the recommendations of the Commission on Mathe-matics of the College Entrance Examination Board and the courses of study proposed by the School Mathematics Study Group and numerous other syllabi. The treatment of limits, continuity, and series is intuitive. The exposition is clear and the book could be used for self study by qualified high school students. This book is highly recommended for those college freshmen whose mathematics preparation did not include some of the modern courses and ideas.

10. Kelley, John L.: INTRODUCTION TO MODERN ALGEBRA, Van Nostrand, 1960.

This is the official textbook for the 1960 Continental Classroom Presentation on NBC television. The text presupposes a knowledge of elementary high school algebra and high school plane geometry. It is designed for a first year course in a liberal arts college program. Many recommendations of professional groups concerned with the mathematical curriculum have been embodied in the text, and therefore it may be useful for teachers of high school mathematics.

11. Larsen, Harold E.: ARITHMETIC FOR COLLEGES, Macmillan, 1958.

The title of this book is somewhat misleading. It would appear at first glance to be another book intended to develop quantitative skill in weak students. However this is not the case. This book appears to be an excellent text for teaching the concepts of mathematics that an elementary school teacher needs. For example, the book contains ancient and modern systems of notation, casting out nines, tests of divisibility, precision and accuracy, some geometry and an introduction to the slide rule. Scattered throughout are a number of recreational problems.

12. Lay, L. Clark: ARITHMETIC: AN INTRODUCTION TO MATHEMATICS, Macmillan, 1961.

The book was written for those who have had instruction in arithmetic in the elementary grades but find themselves not prepared to begin the study of algebra. However it appears to be of even greater value to those who are planning to teach elementary arithmetic. The book is written from the viewpoint of modern mathematics in that attention has been given to vocabulary and careful definitions. According to the author the best way to help students raise their level of understanding and gain some mathematical maturity is to give them the hardest possible questions about the easiest problems. Two obviously weak sections of the book are the division of decimals and the solution of verbal problems.

13. Marks, John L., C. Richard Purdy, and Lucien B. Kinney: TEACHING ELEMENTARY SCHOOL MATHEMATICS FOR UNDERSTANDING, McGraw-Hill, 2nd edition, 1965.

The authors have produced a book that contains a well-balanced combination of content and method. Sample lessons and testing techniques are included. A separate study guide is also available.

14. May, Kenneth O.: ELEMENTS OF MODERN MATHEMATICS, Addison-Wesley, 1959.

The stated purpose of the author is to help the student obtain a modest mathematical literacy. The book includes the topics of elementary algebra, logic, theory of sets, analytic geometry, functions, numbers, probability and statistics.

15. Meserve, Bruce and M. A. Sobel: MATHEMATICS FOR SECONDARY SCHOOL TEACHERS, Prentice-Hall, 1962.

Teachers will find this book an effective aid to individual study. To this end the authors have included numerous exercises, with answers in the book, so that practical experience with applications of the contents may be obtained. The book will be equally effective for teachers who wish to study together in small, informal groups. The mathematics included runs from arithmetic to topology and includes many of the modern ideas such as modular arithmetic, congruences, groups, rings, and probability. It is highly recommended for anyone who wishes to fill in some gaps in his mathematics education.

16. Miller, Leslie H.: UNDERSTANDING BASIC MATHEMATICS, Holt, Rinehart and Winston, 1961.

In the author's own words, "This book was prepared for college students who require a review of fundamental mathematics. It can be used as a classroom text or for individual self study. Algebraic topics are given most attention but significant space is devoted to arithmetic, geometry, analytic geometry, and trigonometry." Each chapter opens with an introduction containing a diagnostic test and closes with a summary and an achievement test. Throughout the text there is a gradual increase of the level of mathematical rigor.

17. Moore, John T.: FUNDAMENTAL PRINCIPLES OF MATHE-MATICS, Rinehart, 1960.

The development of the various topics is orderly and in agreement with the recommendations of various committees studying the mathematics curriculum. The author has succeeded in keeping in mind the needs of the young mathematician, the future engineer, and the scientist. Although the style is a little on the formal side, it reads well. An unusual feature is that answers to the graphing exercises are also included.

18. Osborn, Roger, M. V. De Vault, C. C. Boyd, and W. R. Houston: EXTENDING MATHEMATICS UNDERSTANDING, Charles E. Merrill Books, 1961.

This book is designed to develop and strengthen the mathematical competence of elementary school teachers. It is also useful for supervisors and administrators in that it gives them an idea of the topics included in modern mathematics. Two chapters are especially outstanding, one entitled "Developing Historical Perspectives" and another called "Understanding the Broader Applications of Mathematics."

19. Peterson, John A. and Joseph Hashisaki: THEORY OF ARITH-METIC, John Wiley and Sons, 1963.

Recently, mathematicians have become actively interested in participating in the extremely important task of training elementary school teachers. In general, they considered that accurate knowledge of subject matter is an essential prerequisite to teaching arithmetic. It is with this point of view that "Theory of Arithmetic" was designed for a course to be taught to future elementary school teachers by staff members of a mathematics department at a university or college.

20. Richardson, Moses: FUNDAMENTALS OF MATHEMATICS, Macmillan, 3rd edition, 1966.

This book includes the ABC's of mathematics and a lot more. It should satisfy the appetite of the reader who wishes to pursue the subject in greater detail. In addition it is an excellent source book because it contains historical sidelights, portraits and photographs, and a selected bibliography of 218 items.

21. Sloan, Robert W.: AN INTRODUCTION TO MODERN MATHE-MATICS, Prentice-Hall, 1960.

This small volume provides a readable introduction to recent advances in modern mathematics, including symbolic logic, miniature axiomatic systems, truth sets, open sentences and functions. The book has been found particularly useful for two groups of people: high school students who are interested in modern mathematics but do not hear of it in their classes, and college freshmen and sophomores who have come through the traditional courses in algebra and trigonometry and desire to fill in gaps for themselves.

22. Stoll, Robert R.: SETS, LOGIC, AND AXIOMATIC THEORIES, W. H. Freeman, 1961.

This is an excellent little book on logic and is highly recommended for high school teachers and students as well as for college students. It is felt that the latter could especially benefit from reading this book since most of these topics are not taught in the average course of study.

23. Thorpe, Cleota B.: TEACHING ELEMENTARY ARITHMETIC, Harper and Row, 1962.

Stressing increased rigor in the elementary arithmetic curriculum, Part I describes procedures which give better comprehension of our number system and its operations, which provide a balance between the mathematical and social aspects of arithmetic, and which create interest in the quantitative aspects of pupil exercises. Part II reviews the computational and problem solving processes, serving as a refresher course for the prospective teacher and as a test of his ability to apply the rationale of arithmetic discussed in Part I. The text emphasizes the development and use of equations and the need for manipulative and concrete materials as aids in the introduction of new processes.

24. Youse, Bevan K.: ARITHMETIC: A MODERN APPROACH, Prentice-Hall, 1963.

According to the author, this text was written from notes used over a three-year period in a course for in-service elementary school teachers and for college students majoring in elementary education. Its primary aim is to examine and clarify basic concepts and basic techniques of arithmetic. It is to be noted that this book is on mathematics and not on education. It covers the various topics needed by the elementary school teacher very well.

The following titles of professional books, pamphlets and magazines are selected because of the contribution they can make to the elementary classroom teacher who wishes to build a background of understanding for the changes in elementary school mathematics.

"Analysis of Research in the Teaching of Mathematics," U. S. Department of Health, Education and Welfare, Office of Education, Bulletin No. 8, 1960.

Banks, J. Houston: LEARNING AND TEACHING ARITHMETIC, Allyn and Bacon, 1959.

Brumfiel, Charles F., Robert E. Eicholz, and Merrill E. Shanks: FUNDAMENTAL CONCEPTS OF ELEMENTARY MATHEMATICS, Addison-Wesley, 1962.

"Educational Leadership," Association for Supervision and Curriculum Development, National Education Association, 1201 16th Street N. W., Washington, D. C., March 1962.

"Evaluation in Mathematics," Twenty-sixth Yearbook, National Council of Teachers of Mathematics, 1201 16th Street N. W., Washington, D. C., 1961.

"Frontiers in Mathematics Education," Department of Public Instruction, Lansing, Michigan, Bulletin No. NDEA-310, 1961.

Glennon, Vincent J. and C. W. Hunnicutt, "What Does Research Say About Arithmetic?" Association for Supervision and Curriculum Development, National Education Association, 1201 16th Street N.W., Washington, D. C., 1958.

Grade Teacher Magazine, "A Mathematics Roundup," (Reprint), Darien, Conn., April 1962.

Greater Cleveland Mathematics Program, "Key Topics for Primary Teachers," Science Research Associates, 1962.

"The Growth of Mathematical Ideas: Grades K-12," Twenty-fourth Yearbook, National Council of Teachers of Mathematics, 1201 16th Street N.W., Washington, D. C., 1953.

"Instruction in Arithmetic," Twenty-fifth Yearbook, National Council of Teachers of Mathematics, 1201 16th Street N.W., Washington, D. C., 1960.

Johnson, Donovan A. and William H. Glenn: EXPLORING MATHE-MATICS ON YOUR OWN, Webster Publishing Company, St. Louis, Mo., 1960.

Subtitles of interest to the elementary school teacher in this series of bulletins are:

1. Sets, Sentences, and Operations.
2. Invitation to Mathematics.
3. Understanding Numeration Systems.
4. Fun With Mathematics.
5. Number Patterns.
6. The World of Measurement.
7. Adventures in Graphing.

Jones, Philip S.: "Understanding Numbers: Their History and Use,"

Ulrich's Bookstore, 547-549 E. University Avenue, Ann Arbor, Michigan, 1954.

"The Learning of Mathematics: Its Theory and Practice," Twenty-first Yearbook, National Council of Teachers of Mathematics, 1201 16th Street N.W., Washington, D. C., 1953.

May, Lola J.: "Major Concepts of Elementary Modern Mathematics," John Colburn Associates, 1122 Central Avenue, Wilmette, Ill., 1962.

Mueller, Francis J.: ARITHMETIC—ITS STRUCTURE AND CONCEPTS, Prentice-Hall, 1956.

"The New Mathematics," Department of Audiovisual Instruction, National Education Association, 1201 16th Street N.W., Washington, D. C., March 1962.

"Research Problems in Mathematics Education," U.S. Department of Health, Education and Welfare, Office of Education, Cooperative Research Monograph No. 3, 1960.

"The Revolution in School Mathematics," National Council of Teachers of Mathematics, 1201 16th Street, N.W., Washington, D. C., 1960.

Schaaf, William L.: BASIC CONCEPTS OF ELEMENTARY MATHEMATICS, John Wiley and Sons, 1960.

Swain, Robert L.: UNDERSTANDING ARITHMETIC, Rinehart, 1957.

"Thinking in the Language of Mathematics," Illinois Curriculum Program: The Subject Field Series, Superintendent of Public Instruction, Springfield, Ill., Bulletin C-2, 1959.

Weaver, J. Fred and Cleo Fisher Brawley: "Enriching the Elementary School Mathematics Program for More Capable Children," Boston University Journal of Education, October 1959.

**Supplementary Work**                                    **221**

# Index of Symbols*

| | | |
|---|---|---|
| $\in$ | Is a member of | (17) |
| $U$ | The universe of discourse | (20) |
| $\varnothing$ | The empty set | (20) |
| $\cup$ | Union—a binary operation on sets | (22) |
| $\cap$ | Intersection—a binary operation on sets | (76) |
| $\subset$ | Is a proper subset of | (137) |
| $\subseteq$ | Is a subset of | (79) |
| $A'$ | The complement of the set $A$ | (125) |

$n(A)$  The number of elements in the set $A$—cardinal number of $A$ (23)

| | | |
|---|---|---|
| $\approx$ | Is equivalent to | (135) |

$\aleph_0$  Aleph null—the cardinal number of a countably infinite set (136)

| | | |
|---|---|---|
| $+$ | Addition, a binary operation | (31) |
| $-$ | Subtraction, the inverse of addition | (35) |
| $\times$ | Multiplication, a binary operation | (36) |
| $\div$ | Division, the inverse of multiplication | (48) |
| $>$ | Is greater than | (23) |
| $<$ | Is less than | (23) |
| $\geq$ | Is at least equal to | (24) |
| $\leq$ | Is at most equal to | (77) |
| $\leftrightarrow$ | Corresponds to | (27) |
| GCD | Greatest common divisor | (113) |
| LCM | Least common multiple | (116) |

$3^{-1}$  That number which when multiplied by 3 yields 1, that is, $\frac{1}{3}$; also called the reciprocal of 3 (95)

*The number in parentheses is the page on which the symbol first appears.

| | | |
|---|---|---|
| $10^4$ | $10 \times 10 \times 10 \times 10$ | (68) |
| $\sqrt{a}$ | Square root of $a$, that is, that number which when multiplied by *itself* will yield $a$ | (96) |
| $\overleftrightarrow{AB}$ | Line $AB$—the line containing the two points $A$ and $B$ | (55) |
| $\overrightarrow{AB}$ | Ray $AB$—a half-line including the end-point at $A$ | (56) |
| $\overline{AB}$ | Line segment $AB$, having end-points at $A$ and $B$ | (56) |
| $\parallel$ | Is parallel to | (165) |
| $\perp$ | Is perpendicular to | (165) |
| $\angle$ | Angle | (100) |
| $\triangle$ | Triangle | (104) |
| $\cong$ | Is congruent to | (157) |
| $\sim$ | Is similar to | (158) |
| $\doteq$ | Is approximately equal to | (97) |

# Answers and Hints to Exercises

**Chapter 1** (page 27)

1. (a) To make mathematics more interesting by giving logical explanations and using experimentation and discovery.
   (b) To teach mathematics more efficiently to more people.
   (c) To develop the methods of communication in mathematics.
   (d) To develop the foundation and attitudes necessary for further learning.
   (e) To develop an appreciation for mathematics.

3. {the four greatest athletes of all time}

4. {states in the United States}

5. (a) No elements (empty set, $\varnothing$)
   (b) Finite number of elements
   (c) Infinite number of elements

6. $A = \{7, 8, 9, \ldots\}$
   $B = \{1, 2, 3, \ldots, 10\}$
   $A \cup B = \{1, 2, 3, 4, \ldots\}$

7. In exercise 6,
   $n(A) = $ countably infinite
   $n(B) = 10$
   $n(A \cup B) = $ countably infinite

8. $E$ is not the empty set, that is, $E$ contains at least one element.

9. (a) $R \cup S$ is the set of students who are either redheaded boys *or* girls wearing red skirts.
   (b) $R \cup U$ is $U$
   (c) $S \cup \varnothing$ is $S$

10. Show that there exists a one-to-one correspondence by matching the elements

$$
\begin{array}{ccccc}
1 & 2 & 3 & \cdots & n & \cdots \\
\updownarrow & \updownarrow & \updownarrow & & \updownarrow & \\
1\,000\,000 & 2\,000\,000 & 3\,000\,000 & \cdots & 1\,000\,000n & \cdots
\end{array}
$$

11. $M \cup T = \{2, 3, 4, 5, 6, 10, 12, 13, 31\}$

12. The set $A \cup B$ is derived from sets $A$ and $B$, that is, $A \cup B$ is the set of elements which are members of at least one of the given sets. The whole $(A \cup B)$ cannot be greater than its parts $(A$ and $B)$.

13. (a) $A$, $B$ are both the empty set $\varnothing$
    (b) $A$ (or $B$) is the empty set $\varnothing$
    (c) The finite sets $A$ and $B$ have no elements in common
    (d) $A$ and $B$ are countably infinite sets
    (e) $A$ is countably infinite and $B$ is finite (exercise 6)

14. $101 \notin \{2, 4, 6, \ldots\}$ since 101 is not divisible by 2.

15. $\{$Olympic champions$\}$ is well defined if we define "champions" as gold medal winners, since names can be found in records—at least in recent years.

16. $\varnothing = \{$odd natural numbers divisible by 2$\}$

17. $U = \{1, 2\}$

18. $W \cup V = \{7, 6, 23, 5, 2, 4, 1, 9, 22, 8\}$; $n(W \cup V) = 10$

19. In exercise 18,
    $n(\varnothing) < n(V)$.

20. $A \cup B = \varnothing$ if and only if $A = \varnothing$ and $B = \varnothing$.

## Chapter 2 (page 52)

1. $4 + 6 = 10$ and $4 \times 6 = 24$ are the only natural numbers; $4 \div 6 = \frac{2}{3}$ and $4 - 6$ are not natural numbers.

2. Zero is not defined as a natural number.

3. Three—properties **A1**, **M1**, and **D**.

4. Yes, since multiples of 10 are 10, 20, 30, . . . and adding any two of these will result in a multiple of 10 because of **A1**. For example, using D, $20 + 30 = (2 \times 10) + (3 \times 10) = (2 + 3) \times 10 = 5 \times 10 = 50$.

5. Renaming 27 as $19 + 8$ shows that the student was aware of the fact that $27 - 19 = 8$.

6. A select group of numbers was taken to attempt to show closure under division. One counterexample would prove that natural numbers are not closed under division. For example, $2 \div 5$ is not a natural number.

**7.** To prove that a property does not hold it is sufficient to find a single situation in which it does not hold.

$$6 - 4 = 2 \text{ is a natural number}$$
$$4 - 6 \text{ is not a natural number.}$$

**8.** Consider $13 - 9 - 2$; on the one hand, $(13 - 9) - 2 = 2$ while on the other hand, $13 - (9 - 2) = 6$. Thus the associative property does not hold for natural numbers when the operation is subtraction.

**9.** Is $a \div (b - c) = (a \div b) - (a \div c)$ always true? Look at an example.

$$16 \div (4 - 2) \neq (16 \div 4) - (16 \div 2)$$
$$16 \div 2 \quad \neq \quad 4 \quad - \quad 8$$
$$8 \quad \neq \quad 4 \quad - \quad 8.$$

**10.** $6 \div 3 = 2$ a natural number
$3 \div 6 \quad$ is not a natural number.

**11.** By **M4**, $a \times 1 = a$ for any natural number $a$. Since division is the inverse of multiplication, $a \div 1 = a$ for every natural number $a$. Note also that $1 \times a = a$ leads to $a \div a = 1$ for every natural number $a$.

**12.** (a) 89 (b) 139 (c) 365 (d) 178 (e) 209.

**15.** (a)
$$\begin{array}{r} 36 \\ -27 \\ \hline \end{array} \quad \begin{array}{r} 20 + 16 \\ -(20 + 7) \\ \hline 9 \end{array}$$
(b)
$$\begin{array}{r} 92 \\ -59 \\ \hline \end{array} \quad \begin{array}{r} 80 + 12 \\ -(50 + 9) \\ \hline 30 + 3 \text{ or } 33 \end{array}$$

(c)
$$\begin{array}{r} 102 \\ -87 \\ \hline \end{array} \quad \begin{array}{r} 90 + 12 \\ -(80 + 7) \\ \hline 10 + 5 \text{ or } 15 \end{array}$$
(d)
$$\begin{array}{r} 113 \\ -76 \\ \hline \end{array} \quad \begin{array}{r} 100 + 13 \\ -(70 + 6) \\ \hline 30 + 7 \text{ or } 37 \end{array}$$

(e)
$$\begin{array}{r} 100 \\ -69 \\ \hline \end{array} \quad \begin{array}{r} 91 + 9 \\ -(60 + 9) \\ \hline 31 + 0 \text{ or } 31 \end{array}$$

**16.** (a)
$$\begin{array}{r} 36 \\ -27 \\ \hline \end{array} \quad \begin{array}{r} 30 + 6 \\ -(25 + 2) \\ \hline 5 + 4 \text{ or } 9 \end{array}$$
(b)
$$\begin{array}{r} 92 \\ -59 \\ \hline \end{array} \quad \begin{array}{r} 60 + 32 \\ -(58 + 1) \\ \hline 2 + 31 \text{ or } 33 \end{array}$$

(c)
$$\begin{array}{r} 102 \\ -87 \\ \hline \end{array} \quad \begin{array}{r} 100 + 2 \\ -(85 + 2) \\ \hline 15 + 0 \text{ or } 15 \end{array}$$
(d)
$$\begin{array}{r} 113 \\ -76 \\ \hline \end{array} \quad \begin{array}{r} 107 + 6 \\ -(70 + 6) \\ \hline 37 + 0 \text{ or } 37 \end{array}$$

**17.** (a) $16 \times 7 = (10 + 6) \times 7 = (10 \times 7) + (6 \times 7)$
$$= 70 + 42 = 112$$

(b) $39 \times 8 = (30 + 9) \times 8 = (30 \times 8) + (9 \times 8)$
$$= 240 + 72 = 312$$

(c) $9 \times 62 = 9 \times (60 + 2) = (9 \times 60) + (9 \times 2)$
$\qquad = 540 + 18 = 558$

(d) $27 \times 6 = (20 + 7) \times 6 = (20 \times 6) + (7 \times 6)$
$\qquad = 120 + 42 = 162$

(e) $89 \times 8 = (80 + 9) \times 8 = (80 \times 8) + (9 \times 8)$
$\qquad = 640 + 72 = 712$

(f) $36 \times 24 = (30 + 6) \times (20 + 4)$
$\qquad = (30 \times 20) + (30 \times 4) + (6 \times 20) + (6 \times 4)$
$\qquad = 600 + 120 + 120 + 24$
$\qquad = 864$

**18.** (a)
```
    16
  × 7
  ────
    42
  + 70
  ────
   112
```
(b)
```
     39
   × 8
   ────
     72
  +240
   ────
   312
```
(c)
```
      9
   ×62
   ────
     18
  +540
   ────
    558
```
(d)
```
    27
  × 6
  ────
    42
 +120
  ────
   162
```
(e)
```
     89
   × 8
   ────
     72
  +640
   ────
    712
```
(f)
```
     36
   ×24
   ────
     24
    120
    120
    600
   ────
    864
```

**19.** (a) 28 | 367  = 13 R 3
```
      367  | = 13 R 3
      280  | 11
      ───
       87
       84    3
      ───
        3
```

(b) 17 | 92 = 5 R 7
```
       92  | = 5 R 7
     −119  |   7
     ───     ─
       85    5
      ───
        7
```

(c) 106 | 861 = 8 R 13
```
      861  | = 8 R 13
      848  |  8
      ───
       13
```

(d) 69 | 902 = 13 R 5
```
      902  | = 13 R 5
      690  |  10
      ───
      212
      207     3
      ───
        5
```

(e) 67 | 1893 = 28 R 17
```
     1893  | = 28 R 17
     1340  |  20
     ────
      553
      536     8
     ────
       17
```

(f) 493 | 3967 = 8 R 23
```
     3967  | = 8 R 23
     3944  |  8
     ────
       23
```

**20.** (a) $26 - 7 = 19$
(b) $520 \div 8 = 65$
(c) $23 + 16 = 39$
(d) $29 \times 37 = 1073$
**21.** (b) $4n$

## Chapter 3 (page 62)

**1.**

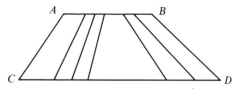

The points of $AB$ can be matched with the points of $CD$.

**2.** (a) $\overrightarrow{RT}$ or $\overrightarrow{RS}$
(b) $\overrightarrow{RS}$ or $\overrightarrow{RT}$
(c) $\overrightarrow{TR}$ or $\overrightarrow{TS}$
(d) $\overrightarrow{RS} \cup \overrightarrow{TR} = \overleftrightarrow{RT}$
(e) $RS$
(f) no

**3.** The union of all lines parallel to $\overleftrightarrow{RT}$ is the plane of the page.

**4.** The union of the two half-planes formed by $\overleftrightarrow{RT}$ is the plane of the page.

**5.** Points which are not connected by a line segment may be studied in zero-dimensional geometry. As the line is a step down from the plane, unconnected points are a step down from the line.

**6.** The measure of a line segment is zero if the end-points coincide.

**7.** (Note: measure will change as drawings are changed.)
(a) $FG$ of Section 2 : 1¾
(b) $GE$ of Section 2 : 1
(c) $EF$ of Section 2 : 2½
(d) $FE$ of Section 2 : 2½
(e) $AB$ of Section 3 : 3
(f) $AC$ of Section 3 : 1¾
(g) $CB$ of Section 3 : 2
(h) $1¾ + 2 > 3$
   $3¾\quad > 3$
(i) If the point $C$ is on the line segment $AB$.

## Chapter 4 (page 74)

**1.** 2, 3, 5, 7, 11, 13, 17, 19, 23, 29, 31, 37, 41, 43, 47, 53, 59, 61, 67, 71, 73, 79, 83, 89, 97.

**2.** 2,3; 3,5; 5,7; 11,13; 17,19; 29,31; 41,43; 59,61; 71,73.

**3.** (a) $81 = 9 \times 9 = 3 \times 3 \times 3 \times 3 = 3^4$
   (b) $441 = 9 \times 49 = 3 \times 3 \times 7 \times 7 = 3^2 \times 7^2$
   (c) $100 = 10 \times 10 = 5 \times 2 \times 5 \times 2 = 2^2 \times 5^2$
   (d) $225 = 25 \times 9 = 5 \times 5 \times 3 \times 3 = 3^2 \times 5^2$
   (e) $1\,000\,000 = 1000 \times 1000 = 100 \times 100 \times 100$
   $$= 5^6 \times 2^6$$

**4.** There are nine prime numbers between 101 and 150: 103, 107, 109, 113, 127, 131, 137, 139, 149.

**5.** There are 38 composite numbers between 150 and 200: 152, 153, 154, 155, 156, 158, 159, 160, 161, 162, 164, 165, 166, 168, 169, 170, 171, 172, 174, 175, 176, 177, 178, 180, 182, 183, 184, 185, 186, 187, 188, 189, 190, 192, 194, 195, 196, 198.

**6.** Prime.

**7.** (a)                           (b)

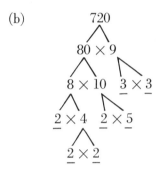

$2 \times 3 \times 5^2$

$2^4 \times 3^2 \times 5$

(c)                           (d)

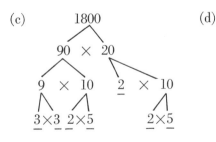

$2^3 \times 3^2 \times 5^2$                    $3 \times 5 \times 7^2$

**8.** (a) $4^3 \times 3 = 64 \times 3 = 192$
   (b) $2^2 \times 3^3 = 4 \times 27 = 108$
   (c) $2^2 \times 3^2 \times 5^2 = 4 \times 9 \times 25 = 900$
   (d) $7^3 \times 2^4 = 343 \times 16 = 5488$

**9.** $39\,605 = (3 \times 10^4) + (9 \times 10^3) + (6 \times 10^2) + 5.$

**10.** (a) $(302)_5 = (3 \times 5^2) + (0 \times 5) + 2 = (77)_{10}$

(b) $(24)_5 = (2 \times 5) + 4 = (14)_{10}$

(c) $(1234)_5 = (1 \times 5^3) + (2 \times 5^2) + (3 \times 5) + 4$
$$= 125 + 50 + 15 + 4 = (194)_{10}$$

(d) $(42344) = (4 \times 5^4) + (2 \times 5^3) + (3 \times 5^2) + (4 \times 5) + 4$
$$= 2500 + 250 + 75 + 20 + 4$$
$$= (2849)_{10}$$

**11.** (a) $(109)_{10} = (4 \times 25) + (1 \times 5) + 4 = (414)_5$

(b) $(468)_{10} = (3 \times 125) + (3 \times 25) + (3 \times 5) + 3 = (3333)_5$

(c) $(6790)_{10} = (2 \times 3125) + (0 \times 625) + (4 \times 125)$
$$+ (1 \times 25) + (3 \times 5) + (0 \times 1)$$
$$= (204130)_5$$

(d) $(18\,965)_{10} = (1 \times 15\,625) + (1 \times 3125) + (0 \times 625)$
$$+ (1 \times 125) + (3 \times 25) + (3 \times 5) + (0 \times 1)$$
$$= (1101330)_5$$

**12.** $(13242)_5 = (1 \times 5^4) + (3 \times 5^3) + (2 \times 5^2) + (4 \times 5) + (2 \times 1)$
$$= 625 + 375 + 50 + 20 + 2$$
$$= (1072)_{10}$$
Therefore $(1073)_{10} > (13242)_5$

**13.** (a)
$$\begin{array}{r} 314 \\ + \ 43 \\ \hline 412 \end{array}$$

(b)
$$\begin{array}{r} 1340 \\ + \ 444 \\ \hline 2334 \end{array}$$

(c)
$$\begin{array}{r} 2304 \\ + \ 4032 \\ \hline 11341 \end{array}$$

**14.** (a)
$$\begin{array}{r} 23 \\ \times \ 34 \\ \hline 202 \\ 124 \\ \hline 1442 \end{array}$$

(b)
$$\begin{array}{r} 44 \\ \times \ 13 \\ \hline 242 \\ 44 \\ \hline 1232 \end{array}$$

(c)
$$\begin{array}{r} 123 \\ \times \ 30 \\ \hline 000 \\ 424 \\ \hline 4240 \end{array}$$

**15.** (a)
$$\begin{array}{r} 43 \\ -14 \\ \hline 24 \end{array}$$

(b)
$$\begin{array}{r} 103 \\ -32 \\ \hline 21 \end{array}$$

(c)
$$\begin{array}{r} 434 \\ -141 \\ \hline 243 \end{array}$$

**16.** (a) $3131 \div 43$

$$\begin{array}{r} 33 \\ 43 \ \overline{) \ 3131} \\ 234 \\ \hline 241 \\ 234 \\ \hline 2 \end{array}$$

(b) $430 \div 10$

$$\begin{array}{r} 43 \\ 10 \overline{\smash{)}430} \\ \underline{40} \\ 30 \\ \underline{30} \\ \end{array}$$

$$\begin{array}{r} 1 \\ 24 \overline{\smash{)}42} \\ \underline{24} \\ 13 \\ \end{array}$$

(c) $42 \div 24$

17. XIV+ XXI + XL = XXXV + XL
    = XXXV + XXXX
    = XXXXXXXV
    = LXXV

Check:  XIV = 14
        XXI = 21
        XL = 40
      LXXV = $\overline{75}$

18. XLIX = $(49)_{10}$
    = $(1 \times 25) + (4 \times 5) + 4$
    = $(144)_5$

19. XX ÷ V = IV

Check: $\dfrac{20}{5} = (4)_{10} = (4)_5$

20. XXI = 21
    $-V = -5$
    $(16)_{10} = (3 \times 5) + 1 = (31)_5$
    Thus $(32)_5 > $ XXI $-$ V.

## Chapter 5 (page 85)

1. $A = \{1, 3, 5, 7, \ldots\}$
   $B = \{2, 4, 6, 8, \ldots\}$
   $A \cap B = \varnothing$

2. $B \cap R$ is the set of brown-haired girls in the class wearing something red. $R \cap B$ is the set of girls who are wearing something red and also have brown hair. $B \cup R$ is the set of girls in the class who have brown hair *or* are wearing something red or have brown hair *and* are also wearing something red.

**3.** $n(C) = 8$
$$2^n = 2^8 = 256$$

**4.**

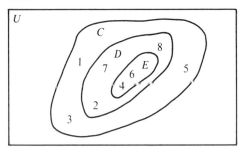

**5.** (a) $C \cap D = D$      (e) $C \cup E = C$
   (b) $D \cap E = E$      (f) $(D \cup E) \cap (E \cap \varnothing) = D \cap \varnothing = \varnothing$
   (c) $C \cap E = E$      (g) $(C \cap D) \cap E = D \cap E = E$
   (d) $D \cup E = D$      (h) $C \cap (D \cap E) = C \cap E = E$

**6.** $M \subseteq N$ and $N \subseteq M$ implies that sets $M$ and $N$ are equal.

**7.** $S \not\subseteq T$ since every element of $S$ cannot be an element of $T$. It does not necessarily follow that $T \subseteq S$ since the elements of $T$ may be different than the elements of $S$.

**8.**

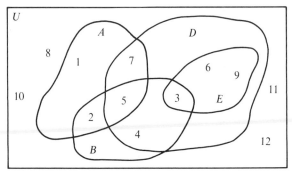

**9.** (a) $5 \in A \cap B \cap D$     (b) $3 \in B \cap E$     (c) $6, 9 \in D \cap E$
      $5 \in A \cap D$         (d) $7 \in A \cap D$     (e) $11 \in U$
      $5 \in B \cap D$

**10.** (a) $(A \cap B) \cap (A \cap D) = \{2,5\} \cap \{5,7\} = \{5\}$
    (b) $(B \cup E) \cap (A \cap D) = \{2,3,4,5,6,9\} \cap \{5,7\} = \{5\}$
    (c) $(A \cap D) \cup (B \cap E) = \{5,7\} \cup \{3\} = \{3,5,7\}$

**11.** If $A = \{2, 1, 5, 7\}$, then its subsets are $\varnothing$, $\{1\}$, $\{2\}$, $\{5\}$, $\{7\}$, $\{2,1\}$, $\{2,5\}$, $\{2,7\}$, $\{1,5\}$, $\{1,7\}$, $\{5,7\}$, $\{2,1,5\}$, $\{2,1,7\}$, $\{1,5,7\}$, $\{2,5,7\}$, $\{2,1,5,7\}$.

**12.** The empty set has one subset, itself; hence $2^0$ may be defined as 1.

                                      **Answers and Hints to Exercises**

**13.**

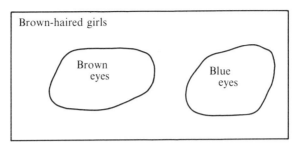

Brown-haired girls

Brown eyes

Blue eyes

**14.** The data is inconsistent since $30 + 32 + 22 + 27 + 16 = 144 > 120$

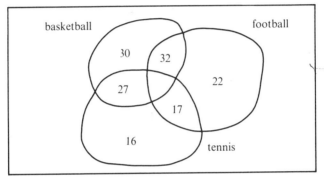

basketball

football

30

32

22

27

17

16

tennis

**15.** *No* boys liked all three sports. Twenty-seven voted for basketball and tennis but not football.

**16.** Yes, since if every element of $A$ is an element of $B$ and if every element of $B$ is an element of $C$, it follows that every element of $A$ must also be an element of $C$.

**17.** $D \cap E \subseteq D \cup E$
The set of elements which are in both $D$ and $E$ is a subset of the set of elements which are in $A$ or $B$ or in both $A$ and $B$.
The statement is correct and can be verified from the definitions or by a Venn diagram.

**18.** (1) Union of the intersection of $A$ and $B$ with $C$.
(2) Intersection of the union of $B$ and $C$ with $A$.
The meaning can be clarified by the use of parentheses.

## Chapter 6 (page 98)

**1.** The distributive property involves two operations, multiplication and addition.

**2.** $4 - 6 = x$

    or

$x + 6 = 4$

No such whole number $x$ exists.

**3.** $4 \div 3 = y$

    or

$y \times 3 = 4$

No such whole number $y$ exists.

**4.** $\frac{8}{2}$, $3 + 3$, $8 - 2$, $2 \times (2 + 1)$, VI, six, 卌 |, ocho, $24 \div 4$, etc.

**5.** $^{23}\!\!/_{7}$ is the 23rd number in the 7th row.

**6.** 3.1416 is the same as $\dfrac{31416}{10000}$.

**7.** $\dfrac{101}{103} = \dfrac{101}{103} \times 1 = \dfrac{101}{103} \times \dfrac{4}{4} = \dfrac{404}{412}$

$\dfrac{203}{206} = \dfrac{203}{206} \times 1 = \dfrac{203}{206} \times \dfrac{2}{2} = \dfrac{406}{412}$

Thus $\dfrac{101}{103} < \dfrac{405}{412} < \dfrac{203}{206}$.

**8.** $\frac{1}{3} - \frac{1}{2} = x$

    or

$x + \frac{1}{2} = \frac{1}{3}$

No such rational number $x$ exists.

**9.** $\frac{1}{10}$, $\frac{7}{22}$, $\frac{3}{16}$, $\frac{5}{41}$, $\frac{1}{19}$.

**10.** Initial guess of 6

$$40 \div 6 = 6.66$$

$$\frac{6 + 6.66}{2} = 6.33$$

$$40 \div 6.33 \doteq 6.319$$

$$\frac{6.33 + 6.319}{2} \doteq 6.324$$

$$40 \div 6.324 \doteq 6.32$$

Thus $\sqrt{40} \doteq 6.32$.

**11.** $15 \times 15 = 225$
$16 \times 16 = 256$
Thus initial guess of 15.8 is reasonable.
$$252 \div 15.8 \doteq 15.94$$
$$\frac{15.8 + 15.94}{2} \doteq 15.87$$
$$252 \div 15.87 \doteq 15.87$$
Thus $\sqrt{252} \doteq 15.87$.

**12.** $15.87 \times 15.87 \doteq 251.86$
Thus $252 - 251.86 = 0.14$.

**13.** Initial guess of 10
$$40 \div 10 = 4$$
$$\frac{10 + 4}{2} = 7$$
$$40 \div 7 \doteq 5.71$$
$$\frac{7 + 5.71}{2} \doteq 6.35$$
$$40 \div 6.35 \doteq 6.29$$
$$\frac{6.35 + 6.29}{2} \doteq 6.32$$
$$40 \div 6.32 \doteq 6.32$$
Thus $\sqrt{40} \doteq 6.32$ as in exercise 10 but one more division was required.

**14.** $\sqrt{72.25}$
$$8 \times 8 = 64$$
$$9 \times 9 = 81$$
Thus initial guess of 8.5 is reasonable.
$$72.25 \div 8.5 = 8.5$$
Therefore $\sqrt{72.25} = 8.5$.

**15.** $\sqrt{9} + \sqrt{4} \neq \sqrt{13}$ since
$\sqrt{9} + \sqrt{4} = 3 + 2 = 5$   and
$5 \times 5 = 25 \neq 13$.

**16.** $\sqrt{9} \times \sqrt{4} = \sqrt{36}$ since
$\sqrt{9} \times \sqrt{4} = 3 \times 2 = 6$   and
$6 \times 6 = 36$.

**Chapter 7** (110)

1. (a) 125°        (b) 20°        (c) 70°
2. (a) ∠CBA        (b) ∠ACB        (c) ∠CAB
3. The exterior angle of 60° is 300°.

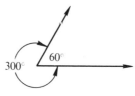

4. Since a right triangle has a 90° angle, $180° - (90° + 20°)$ gives the third angle. Thus the other angles are 90° and 70°.
5.

The two angles opposite the right angle have equal measure.

Thus $\dfrac{180° - 90°}{2} = \dfrac{90°}{2} = 45°$.

Hence the sizes of the angles in an isosceles right triangle are 90°, 45°, 45°.

6.

The two angles opposite the 50° angle have equal measure.

Thus $\dfrac{180° - 50°}{2} = \dfrac{130°}{2} = 65°$.

Hence the other two angles are each 65°.

7.

8. 3, 4, and 5 can be measures of the sides of a right triangle since $3^2 + 4^2 = 5^2$.

5, 6, and 8 cannot be measures of the sides of a right triangle since $5^2 + 6^2 \neq 8^2$.

5, 12, and 13 can be measures of the sides of a right triangle since $5^2 + 12^2 = 13^2$.

9. Yes, since a square always has four right angles but a rectangle may not have four equal sides.

10. There are 12 inches to 1 foot.
There are $12 \times 12$ square inches to $1 \times 1$ square foot, that is, 144 square inches to 1 square foot.

11. There are $12 \times 12$ square inches to $1 \times 1$ square foot. There are $12 \times 12 \times 12$ cubic inches to $1 \times 1 \times 1$ cubic foot, that is, 1728 cubic inches to 1 cubic foot.

12. Obtain a square-bottomed one-quart milk carton and measure the length, width, and height in inches. Multiply these measures to find the approximate number of cubic inches in a quart.

13. A cube has 8 vertices. At each vertex there are three right angles, thus there are 24 right angles in a cube.

14.

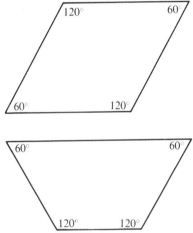

## Chapter 8 (page 123)

1. (a) $2^8$
   (b) $3^5$
   (c) $5 \times 7^2$
   (d) $2^4 \times 3^2 \times 5 \times 7$
   (e) $2^2 \times 491$

2. (a) 1, 2, 3, 4, 5, 6, 8, 10, 12, 15, 16, 20, 24, 30, 40, 48, 60, 80, 120, 240.
   (b) 1, 2, 4, 8, 16, 32, 64, 128, 256, 512, 1024.
   (c) 1, 2, 13, 41, 26, 82, 533, 1066.

(d) 1, 2, 3, 6, 7, 9, 11, 14, 18, 21, 22, 27, 33, 42, 54, 63, 66, 77, 99, 126, 189, 198, 231, 378, 693, 2079, 4158.

(e) 1, 2, 3, 4, 5, 6, 8, 9, 10, 12, 15, 18, 20, 24, 25, 30, 36, 40, 45, 50, 60, 72, 75, 100, 120, 150, 180, 200, 225, 300, 360, 450, 900, 1800.

**3.** (a) 9        (c) 85
    (b) 9        (d) 1

**4.** (a) 1        (b) 1

**5.** (a) 60       (c) 143
    (b) 63       (d) 48

**6.** (a) $(1703)_8$     (c) $(2113)_8$
    (b) $(33)_8$       (d) $(15513)_8$

**7.** (a) 15       (c) 575
    (b) 247      (d) 8491

**8.** (a)
$$\begin{array}{r} 56 \\ +72 \\ \hline 150 \end{array}$$
(b)
$$\begin{array}{r} 65 \\ -47 \\ \hline 16 \end{array}$$
(c)
$$\begin{array}{r} 36 \\ \times 45 \\ \hline 226 \\ 170 \\ \hline 2126 \end{array}$$

(d)
$$4 \overline{)\begin{array}{l} 30 \\ 140 \\ \phantom{1}14 \\ \phantom{11}0 \\ \phantom{11}0 \end{array}}$$

**9.** $(765)_8 = (\overline{5}01)_{10}$

$$\begin{array}{r|l} 5 & 501 \\ 5 & 100 \quad 1 \\ 5 & 20 \quad 0 \\ & 4 \quad 0 \end{array}$$

$(765)_8 = (4001)_5$

**10.**
$$\begin{array}{r|l} 8 & 36798 \\ 8 & 4599 \quad 6 \\ 8 & 574 \quad 7 \\ 8 & 71 \quad 6 \\ 8 & 8 \quad 7 \\ & 1 \quad 0 \end{array}$$

$(36798)_{10} = (107676)_8$

**11.** (a) 11      (b) 61      (c) 87      (d) 231

**12.** (a) 1111101     (b) 1000011     (c) 110000101
    (d) 100000110010

**13.** (a)
$$\begin{array}{r} 1011 \\ +1001 \\ \hline 10100 \end{array}$$

(b)
$$\begin{array}{r} 11111 \\ +101 \\ \hline 100100 \end{array}$$

(c)
$$\begin{array}{r} 1101 \\ -111 \\ \hline 110 \end{array}$$

(d)
$$\begin{array}{r} 10101 \\ -1010 \\ \hline 1011 \end{array}$$

(e)
$$\begin{array}{r} 101 \\ \times 111 \\ \hline 101 \\ 101\phantom{0} \\ 101\phantom{00} \\ \hline 100011 \end{array}$$

(f)
$$\begin{array}{r} 1101 \\ \times 110 \\ \hline 0000 \\ 1101\phantom{0} \\ 1101\phantom{00} \\ \hline 1001110 \end{array}$$

(g)
$$\begin{array}{r} 1001\phantom{000} \\ 1000\,\overline{\smash{\big)}\,1001000} \\ 1000\phantom{000} \\ \hline 1000\phantom{0} \\ 1000\phantom{0} \\ \hline \end{array}$$

**14.** (a) $(155)_8$   (b) $(414)_5$   (c) $(109)_{10}$

**15.** (a) $(111000110101)_2$
(b) $(104022)_5$
(c) $(3637)_{10}$

**16.** $(311)_{10}$  or  $(100110110)_2$

**17.** $(274)_{10}$

**18.** $(264)_{10}$

**19.** $(390)_{10}$

**20.** Divide the octal number by 2 over and over using the octal system of division. Example:

$$\begin{array}{r|r|l} 2 & 265 & \\ \hline 2 & 132 & 1 \\ \hline 2 & 55 & 0 \\ \hline 2 & 26 & 1 \\ \hline 2 & 13 & 0 \\ \hline 2 & 5 & 1 \\ \hline 2 & 2 & 1 \\ \hline & 1 & 0 \end{array}$$

Thus $(265)_8 = (10110101)_2$.
Another way is to convert each digit of the octal number to binary notation. For example, $(2)_8 = (10)_2$; $(6)_8 = (110)_2$; $(5)_8 = (101)_2$. Then putting these together,
$$(265)_8 = (10110101)_2.$$

**Chapter 9** (page 138)

1. $A' = \{n \mid n < 7\}$

2. $B' = \{n \mid n \leq 3 \quad \text{or} \quad n > 8\}$

3. (a) $\{n \mid n > 3\}$
   (b) $\{n \mid 7 \leq n \leq 8\}$
   (c) $\{n \mid n \leq 3\}$
   (d) $\{n \mid n < 7 \quad \text{or} \quad n > 8\}$
   (e) $\{n \mid n < 7 \quad \text{or} \quad n > 8\}$
   (f) $\{n \mid n \leq 3\}$

4. (a) $\{n \mid n > 8\}$
   (b) $\{n \mid n \leq 8\}$
   (c) $\{n \mid n < 7\}$
   (d) $\{n \mid n \leq 3 \quad \text{or} \quad n > 8\}$

5. $\varnothing' = U$
   *Proof:*
   Let $x \in U$, then $x \notin \varnothing$ since $\varnothing$ has no elements; $x \notin \varnothing$ means $x \in \varnothing'$ by the definition of complementation. Hence $U \subseteq \varnothing'$.
   Let $y \in \varnothing'$, then $y$ must belong to the universal set. That is, $y \in U$. Hence, $\varnothing' \subseteq U$. Since each is a subset of the other $\varnothing' = U$.

6. $(A \cap B)' = \{1, 2, 3, 4, 5, 6, 8, 9, 10\} = A' \cup B'$.

7.

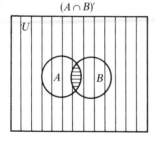

$A \cap B$ is shaded with horizontal lines.
$(A \cap B)'$ is shaded with vertical lines.
Thus it may be seen that $(A \cap B)' = A' \cup B'$.

$A'$ is shaded with horizontal lines.
$B'$ is shaded with vertical lines.
$A' \cup B'$ is total shaded area.

**Answers and Hints to Exercises**

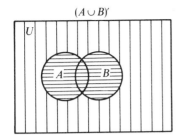

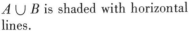

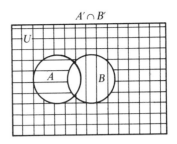

$A \cup B$ is shaded with horizontal lines.
$(A \cup B)'$ is shaded with vertical lines.

$A'$ is shaded with vertical lines.
$B'$ is shaded with horizontal lines.
$A' \cap B'$ is shaded area with both horizontal and vertical lines.

Thus it may be seen that $(A \cup B)' = A' \cap B'$.

8. To show $(A \cup B)' = A' \cap B'$.

*Proof:*

Let $x \in (A \cup B)'$; then $x \notin A \cup B$ by complementation of sets. This means $x$ is not an element of $A$ and $x$ is not an element of $B$. By complementation, $x$ is an element of $A'$ and $x$ is an element of $B'$. Thus, by intersection of sets, $x \in A' \cap B'$. Hence $(A \cup B)' \subseteq A' \cap B'$.

Let $y \in A' \cap B'$; then $y \in A'$ and $y \in B'$ by the definition of intersection of sets. By complementation, $y$ is not an element of $A$ and $y$ is not an element of $B$. This means $y$ does not belong to $A$ or $B$. Thus by the union of sets, $y \notin A \cup B$ and, by complementation of sets, $y \in (A \cup B)'$. Hence $A' \cap B' \subseteq (A \cup B)'$. By definition of subsets, $(A \cup B)' = A' \cap B'$.

To show $(A \cap B)' = A' \cup B'$.

*Proof:*

Let $x \in (A \cap B)'$; then $x \notin A \cap B$ by complementation of sets. This means that $x$ is not an element of $A$ or $x$ is not an element of $B$. By complementation, $x$ is an element of $A'$ or $x$ is an element of $B'$. By definition of union, $x \in A' \cup B'$. Hence $(A \cap B)' \subseteq A' \cup B'$.

Let $y \in A' \cup B'$; then $y \in A'$ or $y \in B'$ by definition of union. $y$ is not an element of $A$ or $y$ is not an element of $B$ by complementation. This means that $y$ does not belong to $A$ and $B$. Thus, by definition of intersection, $y \notin A \cap B$ and by complementation $y \in (A \cap B)'$. Hence $A' \cup B' \subseteq (A \cap B)'$. By definition of subsets, $(A \cap B)' = A' \cup B'$.

**9.**

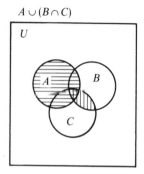

$A \cup (B \cap C)$

$(A \cup B) \cap (A \cup C)$

$A$ is shaded by horizontal lines. $B \cap C$ is shaded by vertical lines. $A \cup (B \cap C)$ is total shaded area.

$A \cup B$ is shaded by vertical lines. $A \cup C$ is shaded by horizontal lines. $(A \cup B) \cap (A \cup C)$ is area with both horizontal and vertical lines.

Thus it may be seen that $A \cup (B \cap C) = (A \cup B) \cap (A \cup C)$.

**10.** To show $A \cup (B \cap C) = (A \cup B) \cap (A \cup C)$.

*Proof:*

Let $x$ be an element of $A \cup (B \cap C)$; then $x$ is an element of $A$ or $x$ is an element of $B \cap C$. If $x$ is an element of $A$, then $x$ is an element of $A \cup B$ and $A \cup C$, thus $x$ is an element of $(A \cup B) \cap (A \cup C)$. Also, if $x$ is an element of $B \cap C$, then $x$ is an element of $B$ and $C$. That is, $x$ is an element of $A \cup B$ and $A \cup C$, thus $x \in (A \cup B) \cap (A \cup C)$. In any case, $A \cup (B \cap C) \subseteq (A \cup B) \cap (A \cup C)$.

Let $y$ be an element of $(A \cup B) \cap (A \cup C)$; then $y$ is an element of $A \cup B$ and $A \cup C$. This means that $y$ is an element of $A$ or of both $B$ and $C$. Hence $y$ is an element of $A \cup (B \cap C)$. Thus $(A \cup B) \cap (A \cup C) \subseteq A \cup (B \cap C)$. By definition of subsets, $A \cup (B \cap C) = (A \cup B) \cap (A \cup C)$.

**11.** (a) $\{(1,2), (1,3), (1,4), (3,2), (3,3), (3,4)\}$.

(b) $\{(2,1), (2,3), (3,1), (3,3), (4,1), (4,3)\}$.

**12.** $\{(3,3)\}$

**13.** $E \cup F = \{2, 3, 5, 6, 8, 10, 12\}$
Cardinal number is 7.

**14.** $E \cap F = \{3, 10\}$
Cardinal number is 2

**15.** $\aleph_0$

**16.**

$$\begin{array}{cccccc}
1 & 2 & 3 & 4 & \cdots & n \\
\updownarrow & \updownarrow & \updownarrow & \updownarrow & & \updownarrow \\
0 & 2 & 4 & 6 & \cdots & (2n-2)
\end{array}$$

Hence $N \approx E$.

$$\begin{array}{cccccc}
1 & 2 & 3 & 4 & \cdots & n \\
\updownarrow & \updownarrow & \updownarrow & \updownarrow & & \updownarrow \\
1 & 3 & 5 & 7 & \cdots & 2n-1
\end{array}$$

Hence $N \approx F$.

$$\begin{array}{cccccc}
1 & 2 & 3 & 4 & \cdots & n \\
\updownarrow & \updownarrow & \updownarrow & \updownarrow & & \updownarrow \\
1000 & 2000 & 3000 & 4000 & \cdots & (n \times 1000)
\end{array}$$

Hence $N \approx T$.

Therefore $N \approx E \approx F \approx T$.

**17.** $G \cap H = H$

$$\begin{array}{cccccc}
1 & 2 & 3 & 4 & \cdots & n \\
\updownarrow & \updownarrow & \updownarrow & \updownarrow & & \updownarrow \\
6 & 12 & 18 & 24 & \cdots & n \times 6
\end{array}$$

$\qquad G \cap H \approx N$

Therefore $G \cap H$ has cardinal number $\aleph_0$.

## Chapter 10 (149)

**1.** (a) $^-1$ (b) $^-5$ (c) $^-1$ (d) $4$ (e) $^-1$

**2.** (a) $^-21$ (b) $^-2\frac{3}{4}$ (c) $^-\frac{1}{2}$ (d) $3$

**3.** $^-\frac{2}{3}$; $5$; $0$.

**4.** $\dfrac{1005}{1012}$ and $\dfrac{1507}{1518}$

**5.** To show $\sqrt{3}$ is not a rational number.

*Proof:*

1. Suppose that $\sqrt{3} = a/b$ where $a \in W$ and $b \in N$ and $a/b$ is in lowest terms.

2. Multiplying both equal numbers by $\sqrt{3}$, we get

$$3 = a^2/b^2.$$

3. Multiplying both equal numbers by $b^2$,

$$3b^2 = a^2.$$

4. Since one of the numbers $(3b^2)$ is a multiple of 3, the other $(a^2)$ must be also.

5. If $a^2$ is a multiple of 3, then $a$ must be a multiple of 3.

6. If $a$ is a multiple of 3, it can be written

$$a = 3k \quad \text{or} \quad a^2 = 9k^2.$$

7. Substituting this value of $a^2$ in step 3 gives

$$3b^2 = 9k^2.$$

8. Dividing both equal numbers by 3,

$$b^2 = 3k^2.$$

9. Since one of the numbers $(3k^2)$ is a multiple of 3, the other $(b^2)$ must be also.

10. If 3 is a factor of $b^2$, then 3 is a factor of $b$.

11. By steps 5 and 10, 3 is a factor of both $a$ and $b$. This contradicts the fact that $a/b$ was written in its lowest terms. Therefore $\sqrt{3}$ must be an irrational number.

6. $\sqrt{5}$

7.

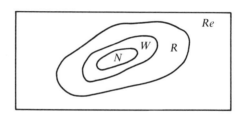

8. $-\frac{3}{2}$

9. (a) $-6 > -7$       (c) $\sqrt{3} > 1.732$
    (b) $3 > -\frac{1}{3}$       (d) $0.333 < \frac{1}{3}$

10. Let $P = \dfrac{\sqrt{2}}{3}$, then $3 \times P = \sqrt{2}$

If $P$ is rational, then $\sqrt{2}$ is rational since $P \times 3$ is rational. Therefore $P$ must be irrational.

## Chapter 11 (page 160)

1. Pentahedron:
$$F + V - E = 5 + 5 - 8 = 2$$
Hexahedron:
$$F + V - E = 6 + 6 - 10 = 2$$

2. Fourteen edges, eight vertices and eight faces.

3. Duplicate the length of the given rectangle on a line segment with a compass. At the end-points of this duplicated length, construct perpendicular line segments. Duplicate the width of the given rectangle on the two constructed perpendicular line segments, setting the compass point on the end-points of the duplicated length. Complete the rectangle by drawing a line segment joining the end-points of the two widths.

4. All points in a plane containing the mid-point of the line segment joining the two given points and perpendicular to the segment.

5.

6. All these triangles are right triangles with the right angle opposite the diameter.

7. The medians meet at a point.

8. The angle bisectors meet at a point.

9. Yes, since a circle is completely determined by its radius and the ratio of the measure of the radius of a circle to the radius of any other circle is a constant as is the circumference.

10. Yes, since the angles of squares are congruent and the ratio of the measure of one side of a square to the measure of a side of any other square is a constant.

11. No, since the ratio of the measures of the lengths of two rectangles is some number but the ratio of the measure of the widths may be a different number.

12.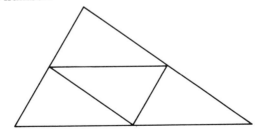

13. Any side of the inner triangle is parallel to a side of the outer triangle; also, the two triangles are similar, the constant ratio being ½. These statements can be proved.
14. The area of the triangle with sides double the length of the corresponding sides of another triangle is four times larger.
15. 3½ inches, 4¼ inches, 5⁶⁷⁄₁₀₀ inches or approximately 5¾.
16.

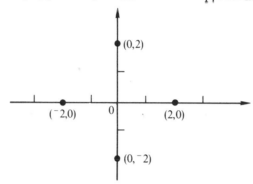

17. A square.
18. All points lie on a circle of radius 5 units with center at the origin.

**Chapter 12** (page 170)

1. $1.111 < \dfrac{10}{9}$ since $\dfrac{10}{9} = 1.1111 \ldots$

2. $\sqrt{2} < \sqrt[3]{3}$ since $\sqrt{2} \doteq 1.414$ and $\sqrt[3]{3} \doteq 1.442$.

3. $9\,5\!\%_{33}$

4. *Proof:*

    1. $A \sim A$ (Reflexive), since the constant ratio is 1.

    2. If $A \sim B$ then $B \sim A$ (Symmetric), since every nonzero number (and the constant ratio is such) has a reciprocal.

    3. If $A \sim B$ and $B \sim C$ then $A \sim C$ (Transitive), since rational numbers are closed under multiplication.

5. The relation $\leq$ is not an equivalence relation since $\leq$ is not symmetric, that is, $a \leq b$ does not imply $b \leq a$.

6. (a) $5 + 3$      (g) huit (French)

    (b) $10 - 2$      (h) $\sqrt{64}$

    (c) $4 \times 2$      (i) $800\%$

    (d) $24 \div 3$      (j) $2 \times (1 + 3)$

    (e) $2^3$      (k) $(13)_5$

    (f) VIII      (l) $(1000)_2$, ⊬⊬⊬ ||| , $\sqrt[3]{512}$, etc.

**Answers and Hints to Exercises**

7. The relation "is a contemporary of" is an equivalence relation since the reflexive, the symmetric and the transitive properties hold as shown by stating the appropriate sentences.

8. $(T00)_{12} = (10 \times 12^2) + (0 \times 12) + (0 \times 1)$
    $= (1440)_{10}$

9. $(T0E)_{12} = (1451)_{10} = (2653)_8$

10. 
```
12 | 6789
   12 | 565    9
      12 | 47   1
          3   11
```
$(6789)_{10} = (3E19)_{12}$

11. $(4302)_5 = (577)_{10} = (401)_{12}$

12. $(110110111)_2 = (439)_{10} = (307)_{12}$

13. $(21300)_5, (1450)_{10}$

14. When adding 6 and 6 in the duodecimal system.

15. $5 - 5; 0 \div 3; 0 \times 4; 0 + 0; 0^3; (0)_5$; zero (French); cero (Spanish); $n(\varnothing); 3 + (^-3)$; etc.

## Chapter 13 (page 187)

1. (a) $5 = 3 + 2$
   (b) $n \leq 7$
   (c) $12 = 4 \times 3$
   (d) $\{x \mid x = 3n \text{ and } n \in N\} \approx \{x \mid x = 4n \text{ and } n \in N\}$
   (e) $N \cap \{x \mid x = ^-n \text{ and } n \in N\} = \varnothing$

2. (a) Negative two is to the left of five on the number line.
   (b) A number is at least two and at most ten.
   (c) The line segment determined by points $A$ and $C$ is perpendicular to the line segment determined by points $A$ and $D$.
   (d) The triangle with vertices at $B$, $C$, and $D$ is similar to the triangle with vertices at $E$, $C$, and $F$.
   (e) Division is not distributive over addition.

3. Sentences (a), (b) and (d) are true.

4. (a) Albany
   (b) Ladis Kovach
   (c) Alaska
   (d) Clara Barton
   (e) Switzerland

5. (a) 2
   (b) 4
   (c) 5
   (d) 5
   (e) 3

**6.** (a) $\{n \le 6 \mid n$ is an integer$\}$     (d) $\{1, 2, 3, 4\}$
   (b) $\varnothing$                                (e) $\{0\}$
   (c) $\{0, 1\}$

**7.** $360 \text{ pupils} \times \dfrac{8 \text{ pencils}}{1 \text{ pupil}} \times \dfrac{1 \text{ gross}}{144 \text{ pencils}} = 20 \text{ gross}$

**8.** $25 \text{ children} \times \dfrac{\frac{1}{2} \text{ pint}}{1 \text{ school day for one child}} \times \dfrac{5 \text{ school days}}{1 \text{ week}} \times$

   $16 \text{ weeks} \times \dfrac{1 \text{ quart}}{2 \text{ pints}} \times \dfrac{1 \text{ gallon}}{4 \text{ quarts}} = 125 \text{ gallons}$

**9.** $250 \text{ pounds} \times \dfrac{16 \text{ ounces}}{1 \text{ pound}} \times \dfrac{1 \text{ fuse}}{2\frac{1}{2} \text{ ounces}} = 1600 \text{ fuses}$

**10.** $2385 \text{ miles} \times \dfrac{29\frac{1}{2} \text{ gallons}}{432 \text{ miles}} \times \dfrac{32.9 \text{ cents}}{1 \text{ gallon}} \times \dfrac{1 \text{ dollar}}{100 \text{ cents}} = \$53.57$

**11.** 27.06; 27.1; 30
**12.** 250 000; 200 000
**13.** 0.078; 0.08; 0.1
**14.** $2.67 \times 3.82 = 10.1994 \doteq 10.2$
   $2.7 \ \times 3.8 \ = 10.26 \ \ \doteq 10.3$
   The two results differ by 0.1.

## Chapter 14 (page 197)

**1.** $(b + c) \times a = (b \times a) + (c \times a)$ for any real numbers $a$, $b$, and $c$.
**2.** Use the associative property for addition on two pairs simultaneously. That is,
$$a + b + c + d = (a + b) + (c + d)$$
**3.** Use the associative property for multiplication repeatedly. That is,
$$a \times b \times c \times d \times e = (a \times b) \times c \times d \times e$$
$$= [(a \times b) \times c] \times d \times e$$
$$= \{[(a \times b) \times c] \times d\} \times e$$
   for any real numbers $a$, $b$, $c$, $d$, and $e$.
**4.** $a \times (b + c + d) = a \times [(b + c) + d] = [a \times (b + c)] + (a \times d) = (a \times b) + (a \times c) + (a \times d)$.
**5.** $3 \div \frac{1}{2} = 6$
**6.** $2.73 \div 0.46 = \dfrac{2.73}{0.46} = \dfrac{2.73}{0.46} \times \dfrac{100}{100} = \dfrac{273}{46} = 5.934^+$
**7.** $80 \times 4 = 320$

**8.** $80.7 \times 4.132 = 80\dfrac{7}{10} \times 4\dfrac{132}{1000}$

$$= \dfrac{807}{10} \times \dfrac{4132}{1000}$$

$$= \dfrac{3\,334\,524}{10\,000}$$

$$= 333.4524$$

**9.** $.0485 = \dfrac{485}{10\,000} = \dfrac{485}{10\,000} \times \dfrac{1/100}{1/100} = \dfrac{485/100}{100} = \dfrac{4.85}{100} = 4.85\%$

**10.** $(23)_5 = (13)_{10} = 1300\%$

**11.** $.001\% = \dfrac{.001}{100} = 0.00001 = \dfrac{1}{100\,000}$

**12.** $385\% = 3.85 = (3.41111\ldots)_5$
(Note—Place values in base five to the right of the quinary point are $\frac{1}{5}, \frac{1}{25}, \frac{1}{125}, \ldots$ or $0.2, 0.04, 0.008, 0.0016, \ldots$)

**13.** $20/47$ since $\dfrac{19}{46} \doteq 0.413$ and $\dfrac{20}{47} \doteq 0.42$

**14.** $n = .999\ldots$
$10n = 9.999\ldots$
$10n - n = 9.999\ldots - .999\ldots$
$9n = 9$
Thus $n = 1 = .999\ldots$

**15.** $4.33333$

**16.** $(23.5)_8 = (2 \times 8^1) + (3 \times 8^0) + (5 \times 8^{-1})$
$= 16 + 3 + .625$
$= (19.625)_{10}$

**17.** $(12.36)_{10} = \left(12 + \dfrac{36}{100}\right)_{10} = \left(14 + \dfrac{44}{144}\right)_8$
$= (14.270^+)_8$

**18.**
```
      43.2
    × 14.3
    ─────────
      2401
      3333
      432
    ─────────
    1344.31
```

**19.** $(14.3)_5 = (9.6)_{10}$
$(43.2)_5 = (23.4)_{10}$
$(1344.31)_5 = (224.64)_{10}$
$23.4 \times 9.6 = 224.64$

**20.** $110.01 \div 11.1 = \dfrac{110.01}{11.1} = \dfrac{110.01}{11\,1} \times \dfrac{100}{100} = \dfrac{11001}{1110} = 1.11001^+$

## Chapter 15 (Self-evaluation) (page 204)

1. They can all be considered as sets of points in a plane.
2. natural (or counting) numbers
3. rational
4. (c)
5. (c)
6. (a)
7. Eighteen is the product of three and six.
8. False
9. a real number
10. True
11. real
12. distributive
13. $\frac{1}{2} = \frac{1}{2} \times 1 = \frac{1}{2} \times \frac{3}{3} = \frac{3}{6}$
14. (b)
15. Each names a unit of length.
16. three
17. False
18. $\{2, 5\}$
19. $\{0, 1, 2, 3, 5, 6, 8, 9, 10\}$
20. $\varnothing$
21. 3 fives and 4 ones, that is, nineteen
22. 5,7; 11,13; 17,19
23. The distributive property.
24. School Mathematics Study Group
25. (c)
26. The emphasis on understanding.
27. 1, 2, 3, 4, 5, 6, 10, 12, 15, 20, 30, 60
28. Multiplying a number by zero always produces zero.
29. (a), (d)

**Answers and Hints to Exercises**

**30.**

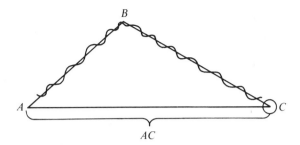

**31.** 3.1623 since $(3.1623)^2 = 10.00014^+ > 10$
**32.** 3.1623 is a rational number since it is a terminating decimal and can be written $^{31623}\!/_{10000}$.
**33.** The set of college students not taking a history course.
**34.** $A \cap C : 4$          $A \cap B = \varnothing$
    $B \cup C : 2, 3, 4, 5$     $(A \cup B)' : 3, 6$
    $C' : 1, 2, 6$
**35.** 9.51
**36.** unary
**37.** binary
**38.** unary
**39.** Distributive property of intersection of sets over union of sets.

**40.** 
$$85 \overline{\big)\, 3753\,} = 44^{13}\!/_{85}$$

$$\begin{array}{r|r} 3753 & \\ 3400 & 40 \\ \hline 353 & \\ 340 & 4 \\ \hline 13 & \end{array}$$

**41.** Multiplicative identity.
**42.** Commutative property of multiplication.
**43.** 26
**44.** Additive identity.
**45.** triangles and rectangles
**46.** $\{7\}$
**47.**

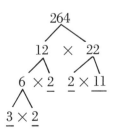

**48.** $2^3 \times 3 \times 11 = 264$

**49.** $(3 \times 512) + (7 \times 64) + (0 \times 8) + (4 \times 1) = (1988)_{10}$

**50.** $(11110101)_2$

**51.** equivalent

**52.** $n(A \cap B)$

**53.** 0

**54.** (a) $10 + 6$

(b) $18 - 2$

(c) $2 \times 8$

(d) $32 \div 2$

(e) $2^4$

(f) XVI

(g) seize (French)

(h) $\sqrt{256}$

(i) $1600\%$

(j) $2 \times (5 + 3)$

(k) $(31)_5$

(l) $(20)_8$, $(10000)_2$, sixteen, etc.

**55.** 14

**56.** prime

**57.** are

**58.** are

**59.** False

**60.** Eleven.

**61.** Addition and multiplication.

**62.** Start at three and count two to the left

**63.** Each is equal to one.

**64.** Octal point.

**65.** (a) $>$

(b) $=$

(c) $>$

(d) $<$

(e) $>$

**66.** The sum of any two odd numbers must be an even number.

**67.** zero

**68.** (a) positive rational number

(b) positive rational number

(c) positive irrational number

(d) negative irrational number

(e) positive integer

(f) zero

(g) positive integer

(h) positive rational number

(i) zero

# Index

**Index**